Welding Engineering
Science and Metallurgy

D1614481

WELDING ENGINEERING SCIENCE AND METALLURGY

J. GARDNER

F.R.S.A., M.Inst.Met.

Lecturer responsible for Welding Engineering
Tottenham College of Technology

LONDON
NORMAN PRICE (PUBLISHERS) LTD

NORMAN PRICE (PUBLISHERS) LTD
17 TOTTENHAM COURT ROAD, LONDON, W1P 9DP

2nd edition 1980

ISBN 0 85380 140 1

Printed in Great Britain by
Biddles Ltd., Guildford, Surrey

CONTENTS

CONTENTS

CHAPTER 1

Matter——Elements, Mixtures, Compounds and Metallic Alloys
The Crystalline Nature of Solids——Hot Cracking
Brittle Fracture

MATTER

The Nature of Matter

Ancient Greek philosophers thought that all matter was primarily derived from just four substances: Earth, Water, Air and Fire. But with the development of chemistry over the centuries, embracing the analysis of a host of compounds, it is now acknowledged that all known matter on our earth, and possibly in the universe as a whole, is built up of many pure substances which are called elements.

The States of Matter

Matter may exist as a solid, liquid or a gas, and in order to appreciate the relationship between these three phases we must first understand its structure.

The ultimate particle of all matter is the atom which consists of a positively-charged nucleus surrounded by a negatively-charged cloud formed by electrons revolving around the nucleus.

These positive and negative forces are balanced, so that the atom as a whole is electrically neutral. The number of electrons in orbit will determine the nature and stability of the atom and will be solely responsible for the chemical and physical characteristics of the matter itself.

When atoms combine they form the smallest possible particle of a compound which is given the name **molecule** and which may comprise two, three, four or more atoms, depending on the class of matter. Only in metals do we find just one atom in a molecule.

When matter is in the solid form the molecules have great attraction for each other, and although in a state of continuous vibration they form a set pattern giving the solid a definite shape, which offers resistance to any attempt to change that shape.

The molecular attraction in a liquid is not as great as with a solid, and vibration does not take place in a fixed position, so that the liquid will take the shape of the vessel in which it is placed.

In the case of gases there is very little attraction of the molecules. Thus the gas has no definite shape, and will spread itself evenly throughout any vessel in which it may be contained.

Matter may be defined as "that which occupies space, has weight and is always inactive by itself". It cannot be destroyed, which can be proved by an experiment where ice is accurately weighed and then allowed to change its state to water and then to steam. If the steam is now condensed to water and then changed back to ice, exactly the same amount of matter will be left as at the commencement provided none has been allowed to escape.

1

ELEMENTS, MIXTURES, COMPOUNDS AND METALLIC ALLOYS

When a molecule is built up of one or more identical atoms, the molecule will be that of a substance in its simplest form.

Such a substance is called an **element** which is defined as "a substance which cannot by any known chemical process be decomposed into anything simpler than itself". There are two kinds of elements: **metals** and **non-metals**. The metals include Copper, Gold, Lead and Tin: the non-metals include Argon, Chlorine, Phosphorus and Sulphur.

In all there are 102 different elements, most of which are present in the earth's crust, though at least 10 of these have been recently discovered in connection with nuclear physics, and possibly do not occur naturally. Five elements account for 90 per cent of the earth's surface: Oxygen 50 per cent; Silicon 26 per cent; Aluminium 7 per cent; Iron 4 per cent; and Calcium 3 per cent.

A table of elements with their chemical symbols will be found on page 93 of the Appendix.

When two or more elements come together they may form a mixture or a compound, depending largely upon the elements present, and the temperature at the time of conjunction.

To illustrate the fundamental differences between a mixture and a compound, simple experiments can be devised employing two elements, iron and sulphur, in their finely divided state.

Mixtures

If the two elements, in any proportion, are thoroughly ground together in a mortar, the resultant mass will appear homogeneous, but under a microscope both iron and sulphur particles can be clearly seen. The iron and sulphur, though intermixed, have not combined chemically, therefore they can be separated. A bar magnet placed into the mixture and agitated will attract the particles of iron, but not the sulphur, and so the iron can be recovered.

A small amount of the mixture is now put into a test-tube containing carbon disulphide. The sulphur will be dissolved, and can be recovered later by evaporation, after the liquid has been separated from the iron through a filter.

The foregoing shows that when elements coalesce to form a mixture they always retain their own independent properties.

Compounds

Another mixture is now prepared in the proportion of 7 gm of iron to 4 gm of sulphur. A test-tube containing the mixture is slowly heated in a flame until its contents begin to glow, denoting the beginning of the chemical reaction between the two elements. The flame is now removed, but the glow will spread throughout the mixture without further heating, until the whole is a red-hot mass.

After cooling, the tube is broken, and the black solid which remains is extracted. This new substance is the compound **iron**

sulphide which is entirely different from its parent elements iron and sulphur.

Any attempt to separate the constituents of the newly-formed compound by the method used on the mixture will be of no use; a chemical combination has taken place, and the properties of the individual elements have been replaced by the properties of iron sulphide.

It will be noted that the proportion of iron to sulphur in the mixture was of no consequence; but in the compound the ratio of 7 parts of iron to 4 parts of sulphur by weight was necessary to produce complete chemical combusion. Any excess of either element would remain after the compound was formed.

Conclusion

A mixture can be defined "as a number of elements or compounds in close proximity to each other without creating any chemical interaction", thus allowing separation to take place without great difficulty.

A compound is produced by the atomic combination of elements, yielding substances whose decomposition is difficult to obtain.

A few of the compounds, and their elements, are given below.

COMPOUND	ELEMENTS CONTAINED
Water	Oxygen, Hydrogen
Salt	Sodium, Chlorine
Sand	Oxygen, Silicon
Acetylene	Carbon, Hydrogen
Chalk	Oxygen, Calcium, Carbon
Sugar	Oxygen, Hydrogen, Carbon
Sulphuric Acid	Oxygen, Hydrogen, Sulphur
Nitric Acid	Oxygen, Hydrogen, Nitrogen

METALLIC ALLOYS

Where high electrical conduction or maximum ductility is an essential requirement in engineering practice, metals in their pure form are mostly used. Whereas mechanical properties relating to tensile strength and hardness are greatly improved when two or more pure metals are combined together to form an alloy.

Such alloys if they are to have any metallurgical value should always be produced from metals that will dissolve completely in each other whilst in the molten state thus forming a homogeneous **liquid solution.**

This solubility having been achieved in the liquid phase will often remain in certain groups of alloys after solidification has taken place and therefore the solid phase structure will consist entirely of the alloying metals in **solid solution.**

There are also many alloying elements that will initially combine to achieve **liquid solubility** but will undergo partial precipitation upon solidification with resultant crystal structures made up of varying amounts of **solid solution** and **pure metal.**

In other groups of alloys, however, solubility will cease to exist altogether upon solidification thus allowing the metals forming the alloy to separate out from each other completely to produce their own individual crystals. Whereas, in contrast, certain metals used for alloying purposes will dissolve in each other during the solid phase to such an extent as to form what is known as **inter-metallic compounds.**

These compounds by themselves, however, have limited use in engineering owing to their extreme hardness and brittleness and for this reason they are generally used in conjunction with **solid solutions** to produce important alloys possessing a widely contrasting range of mechanical properties.

THE CRYSTALLINE NATURE OF SOLIDS

If the internal structure of a solid is built up of crystals, it is said to be of a crystalline nature. Many crystalline formations, especially those produced by minerals, are large enough to be seen with the naked eye. Others, such as the crystalline structure of metals, are so small as to be invisible unless viewed under high magnification. The crystals themselves consist of plane facets arranged in a symmetrical pattern and are composed of a vast accumulation of atoms.

The final shape of a crystal, however, will be determined by the internal arrangement of its atoms and if allowed to grow without obstruction will produce a crystal of perfect shape such as the crystal of copper sulphate illustrated in Fig. 1.1.

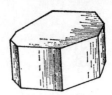

FIG. 1.1.   CRYSTAL OF COPPER SULPHATE.

These perfect shapes are often distorted when the growth of each individual crystal is impeded by that of its neighbours and, therefore, most solids comprise crystals of irregular shapes. When these irregular crystals are in contact on all faces with other irregular crystals they become known as **crystal grains.**

The contact planes form a boundary between adjoining crystal grains and are referred to as **grain boundaries,** as can be clearly seen in Fig. 1.2 which shows the irregular crystal formation of a pure metal.

Solidification of a Pure Metal

When a pure metal begins to solidify, individual crystals will start to take shape at many centres throughout the melt. These

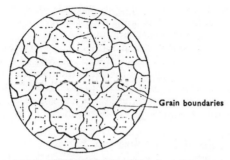

FIG. 1.2. CRYSTAL FORMATION OF A PURE METAL

centres form the crystal nuclei from which the pattern of crystal growth in the form of radial arms begins to develop.

As these arms grow they throw out at periodic intervals secondary arms at right angles to themselves, until a crystal is produced not unlike the branches and twigs of a fir tree. Hence it is sometimes referred to as a **fir tree crystal,** although the correct classification for this type of crystal is a **dendrite.** (Fig. 1.3).

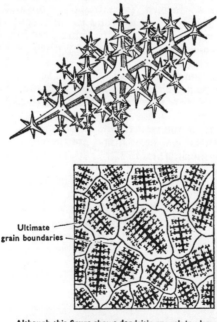

Although this figure shows dendritic growth in plan, it must be remembered that crystal formation always takes place in three dimensions.

FIG. 1.3. DENDRITE CRYSTALS

Upon the continuation of heat extraction from the melt the dendrite will increase in size until the primary and secondary arms come into contact with other similar growths.

This will bring about a restriction in the crystal's progress in that direction, and therefore solidification will now begin to take place in the interstices between the arms themselves. This solidification continues until a crystal is eventually formed without trace of the original skeleton structure, unless severe shrinkage has occurred, or impurities have been trapped in between the arms of the dendrite.

Crystal Formation of a Cast Structure

When molten metal is being cast external solidification will be very rapid as the liquid comes into contact with the walls of the chilled mould into which it has been poured.

This rapid cooling will give rise to the formation of many nuclei, and a polycrystalline layer of chilled crystals will be produced within the outer structure of the ingot.

The conditions prevailing upon further solidification are favourable towards crystals of a new form developing upon the inner boundaries of the chilled crystals.

The direction of growth will now be predominantly inwards towards the centre of the casting, *i.e.* in the opposite direction to which the extraction of heat is taking place.

The crystals so formed are extremely elongated having their lateral growth greatly reduced owing to early contact being made with adjacent crystals growing in the same direction. Such crystals are known as **columnar crystals** and may often be found in some types of weld metal deposits.

The continuation of heat loss throughout the mass will so reduce the internal temperature that simultaneous freezing of the remaining molten metal will now take place. Hence, a third type of crystal will begin to form.

These crystals in the centre zone of the metal do not show any preference to directional growth and are therefore said to be **equiaxed.** They are much larger in size than the surface layer of chilled crystals due to a slower rate of cooling.

The sectional view of a cast ingot (Fig. 1.4) clearly shows the

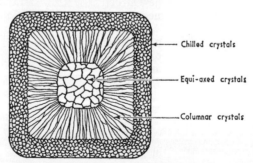

Chilled crystals

Equi-axed crystals

Columnar crystals

FIG. 1.4. AN INGOT OF PURE METAL SHOWING CRYSTAL STRUCTURE

three distinct crystal formations that can be present after solidification of the ingot has been completed.

Recrystallization and Grain Growth

Crystal deformation can have a marked effect upon the mechanical properties of a metal. For instance, when a metal is being rolled in its cold state the crystals of that metal will become greatly elongated in the same direction as the cold working. This granular distortion is shown diagrammatically in Fig. 1.5.

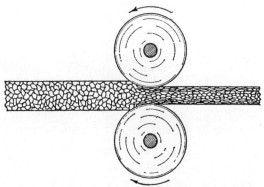

FIG. 1.5. CRYSTAL DISTORTION DUE TO COLD ROLLING

The crystalline structure will now be of a fibrous nature and strain hardening of the metal will become evident.

This undesirable structure can be greatly modified by the application of sufficient heat to produce a new growth of equi-axed crystal grains within the cold worked metal itself as illustrated by the micro-structures in Fig. 5.5. on page 42.

The temperature at which this takes place is known as the **recrystallization temperature** and when the metal has cooled down to normal temperature its new structure will be unstrained and the metal will now have regained those properties it had before cold working took place.

It is quite likely that an improvement in the metal's properties may now be indicated due to a refinement of the crystal grains, provided grain growth has not been allowed to take place.

Grain Growth

The occurrence of grain growth, however, can be due to the excessive heating of a metal to a temperature well above its recrystallization point, thus bringing into being a very coarse granular structure similar to that associated with overheated steel.

Grain growth can also be due to too slow a cooling rate after recrystallization has taken place. It is, therefore, always very important to hold the metal at its recrystallization temperature just long enough to allow the new grain structure to form, and then to control the rate of cooling so that this structure will be one of refined equi-axed crystals.

Enlarged crystal grains will cause a decrease in the ductility and the tensile strength of a metal; but these properties will be enhanced when normal grain size has once again been restored by recrystallization. See Fig. 5.5 on page 42.

HOT CRACKING

The term "hot cracking" generally refers to a discontinuity in the form of a tear that can take place when metal is in its plastic state or at a temperature within a range having a minimum of approximately 1000°C.

This type of crack common to weld metal deposits can always be identified by oxide colouration of the fractured surfaces and will normally appear where structural breakdown along the grain boundaries has occurred due to severe contractional stresses being set up during the cooling cycle. See photograph A on page 101.

Other factors that contribute to hot cracking can be the amount of heat input which not only subjects the metal to grain growth and coarse structures but will also govern the amount of dilution.

The degree of restraint must also be taken into consideration in that it will have an influence upon the crack-sensitivity of the metal itself.

The tendency towards hot cracking can also be greatly increased by the presence of non-metallic impurities as well as various combinations of elements as is often the case with certain non-ferrous and ferrous alloys, especially high alloy steels.

BRITTLE FRACTURE

Brittle fracture, unlike other types of fracture, is essentially one of transgranular breakdown as well as failure along the grain boundaries which can propagate at very high speeds throughout the structure of the metal when often placed under comparatively light loads. Furthermore, this phenomenon need not be influenced by a lack of ductility, for metallurgical tests have shewn that metals having suffered brittle fracture will show a high degree of ductility when then placed under tension.

Plain steels of the low carbon group have proved to be more susceptible to brittle fracture than most other ferrous alloys, especially when these steels have been used in the construction of poorly designed fabrications with service environment at temperatures around zero or below.

The presence of residual stress alone does not appear to be a primary cause of brittle fracture although it is probable that these stresses in conjunction with the other factors already mentioned may serve to initiate such failure particularly when stress concentrations are present in unsound weldments (most fractures of this type normally stem from such defects).

QUESTIONS ON CHAPTER 1

(1) Which one of the following is not a compound:
- (a) Acetylene
- (b) Chalk
- (c) Calcium
- (d) Sulphuric acid?

(2) The first type of crystal that is formed upon the solidification of a metal is classified as:
- (a) A columnar crystal
- (b) A dendrite crystal
- (c) A chilled crystal
- (d) An equi-axed crystal.

(3) When the forming of an alloy produces an INTER-METALLIC COMPOUND. The resultant property will be one of:
- (a) Extreme hardness
- (b) Extreme softness
- (c) High ductility
- (d) High plasticity.

(4) Hot cracking occurs at a minimum temperature of:
- (a) 500°C
- (b) 1000°C
- (c) 1500°C
- (d) 2000°C

(5) Brittle fracture in a metal can be the result of:
- (a) High temperature during service
- (b) Low temperature during service
- (c) Excessive loading during service
- (d) Reduction of ductility during service.

(Answers on page 100)

CHAPTER 2

Oxidation—Reduction—The Formation of Slags
Fluxes and Slags in Welding
Atmosphere Gases and their Effect on Welding
The Inert Gases

OXIDATION

The term oxidation in its simplest form refers to the reaction that takes place when an element comes into contact with oxygen and in so doing forms a compound oxide.

An experiment to illustrate this reaction is the passing of steam over red-hot iron. The oxygen in the steam combines with the iron to form iron oxide during which the liberation of hydrogen takes place:

$$3Fe + 4H_2O \rightarrow Fe_3O_4 + 4H_2.$$

The iron has therefore become oxidized during the process of oxidation.

Oxygen will combine with most metals and with many non-metals. For instance, carbon can be oxidized to carbon dioxide by heating it in concentrated sulphuric acid:

$$C + 2H_2SO_4 \rightarrow CO_2 + 2SO_4 + 2H_2O.$$

Here sulphuric acid has supplied the oxygen and is therefore referred to as an **oxidizing agent.**

An oxidizing agent can be described as a substance able to supply oxygen to metals and non-metals so that they will become oxidized. The most common of these agents, apart from oxygen itself, are compounds containing a high percentage of oxygen such as Nitrates, Chlorates, Dichromates, Persulphates, Permanganates.

The process of oxidation will always produce heat although this is not always apparent because most substances oxidize so slowly that the heat is dissipated as quickly as it is generated. In a few instances, however, oxidation can be so rapid as to produce spontaneous combustion (burning); but in general the reaction at normal temperature is moderately slow and will be intensified only if the temperature is raised whilst oxidation is taking place.

REDUCTION

As mentioned, many metals combine readily with oxygen to form oxides and it is sometimes in this condition that they are found in their natural state as metallic ores. For instance, the ore Bauxite (Al_2O_3) from which aluminium is extracted is predominately an oxide; some other metals whose chief ores are in this category are: iron produced from the ore Hematite (Fe_2O_3); chromium from the ore Chromite (Cr_2O_3); manganese from the ore Braunite (Mn_2O_3); tin from the ore Cassiterite (SnO_2); and copper from its oxide ore Cuprite (Cu_2O).

The refinement of metals necessitates the removal of all forms of matter with which they have combined and if the metallic ores

11

are similar to those of the above group the controlling factor will be the displacement of oxygen. This is achieved by adding a deoxidizer during smelting which has a greater affinity with oxygen than the metal itself and therefore it will reduce the metal to its pure form.

This process of deoxidation is termed **reduction** and the reducing agent will depend on the type of ore under refinement.

THE FORMATION OF SLAGS

The formation of a slag is essential throughout the course of smelting. This is a process used to extract metals from their ores during which oxides and earthy matter, along with dissolved gases, are reduced.

For example, pig iron which is the raw material used in the manufacture of steel, is first obtained from the reduction of iron ore in a blast furnace (Fig. 2.1) which consists of charging iron ore, coke and limestone into the top of the furnace and at the same time injecting a large volume of preheated air in the form of a blast through inlets near the bottom of the furnace.

The combustion of the coke produces the heat and gases which bring about the reduction of the ore at a sufficiently high temperature to melt the resultant iron.

The limestone in the charge, in the form of a flux, has an important part in converting the earthy matter associated with the ore, together with the residue from the coke, into a fusible slag, this being achieved after the limestone has been changed into lime in the heat of the furnace.

This liquid slag floats on the top of the molten iron and is tapped off at regular intervals, whilst the molten iron itself is drawn from the bottom of the furnace.

FLUXES AND SLAGS IN WELDING

During the welding of a metal, oxidation and other unwanted chemical reactions should always be kept to a minimum thereby ensuring the making of a sound weld.

This is made possible by the use of a flux consisting of various chemicals in powder or paste form. The function of this flux must be one of continuous action; apart from removing any non-metallic surface films which may form during the heating cycle, it must also protect the metal from further contamination throughout the entire welding operation.

Its chief characteristic is one of density, because a flux must always be lighter when melted than the molten metal itself, so that any impurities with which it has combined will float to the surface of the molten pool.

Gas welding fluxes must melt at a lower temperature than the metal being welded so that surface oxides will be dissolved before the metal melts.

In the metal arc welding process the consumable electrode used will be coated with a paste consisting of various metallic and non-metallic minerals known collectively as a flux.

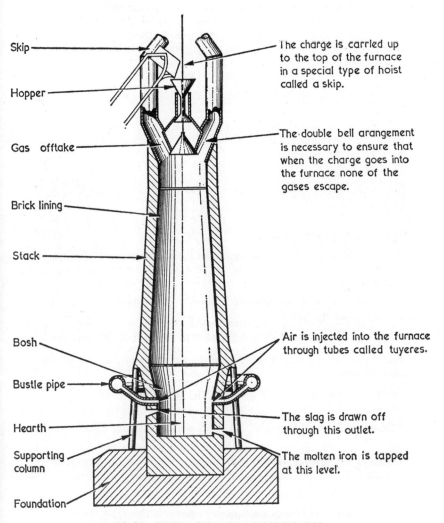

Skip

The charge is carried up to the top of the furnace in a special type of hoist called a skip.

Hopper

Gas offtake

The double bell arangement is necessary to ensure that when the charge goes into the furnace none of the gases escape.

Brick lining

Stack

Bosh

Air is injected into the furnace through tubes called tuyeres.

Bustle pipe

Hearth

The slag is drawn off through this outlet.

Supporting column

The molten iron is tapped at this level.

Foundation

FIG. 2.1. SECTION THROUGH A BLAST FURNACE

When this flux is subjected to elevated temperatures during the welding operation it will combine chemically to form a slag. For example, a flux coating consisting of chemicals such as calcium oxide and silicon dioxide would combine under the heat of the electric arc to form a slag calcium silicate which, being lighter than the molten metal, will float to the top and so protect the weld metal from atmosphere contamination during its transition from a liquid to a solid state.

However, as oxygen can be picked up by the molten metal in the arc region during metal transfer, materials such as ferro-manganese and ferro-silica, which act as deoxidants, are incorporated in the coating.

The properties of the molten slag will vary depending upon the nature of the materials used, thus producing electrodes with different welding characteristics.

The following list indicates some of the naturally occurring minerals, synthetic substances, and materials of organic origin used in the manufacture of electrode coatings, although these can be of a highly complex nature when combined together.

COATING MATERIALS

Titanium Dioxide or Rutile—A natural sand or ground rock which as a major constituent forms a fluid slag, quick freezing, and a good ionizing agent.

Potassium Aluminium Silicate—Improves coating strength, and ionization of the arc.

Cellulose—Increases arc voltage and provides a reducing gas-shield.

Fluorspar—Is used as a fluxing agent, and is useful in controlling slag fluidity.

Metal Carbonates—Provide a reducing atmosphere, and affect the basicity of the slag.

Mineral Silicates—Provide slag, and act as binding agents in the coating.

Iron and Manganese Oxides—Adjust the fluidity and properties of the slag.

Clays and Gums—Give plastic body to electrode coatings.

Bare wire electrodes were always used in the early days of arc welding, and there was severe contamination of the weld metal as well as erratic conditions in the arc stream. During subsequent development it was found that a thin protective flux coating around the bare wire was an improvement. Limestone was one of the first minerals to be used for this purpose because it gave off a protective gas carbon dioxide during decomposition. These early coatings did not contribute a great deal to the welding properties and they were very poor compared with the coatings now available. Modern coatings are of great importance: see Fig. 2.2.

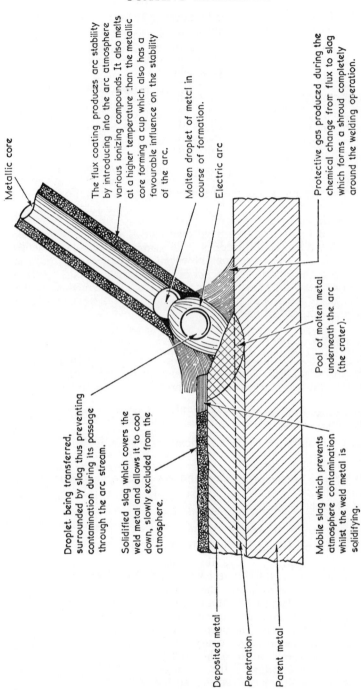

Metallic core

The flux coating produces arc stability by introducing into the arc atmosphere various ionizing compounds. It also melts at a higher temperature than the metallic core forming a cup which also has a favourable influence on the stability of the arc.

Molten droplet of metal in course of formation.

Electric arc

Protective gas produced during the chemical change from flux to slag which forms a shroud completely around the welding operation.

Droplet being transferred, surrounded by slag thus preventing contamination during its passage through the arc stream.

Solidified slag which covers the weld metal and allows it to cool down, slowly excluded from the atmosphere.

Pool of molten metal underneath the arc (the crater).

Mobile slag which prevents atmosphere contamination whilst the weld metal is solidifying.

Deposited metal

Penetration

Parent metal

The composition of the weld metal can be controlled by including various metallic substances in the electrode coating.

FIG. 2.2. THE METALLIC ARC (FUNCTIONS OF THE COATING)

ATMOSPHERE GASES AND THEIR EFFECT ON WELDING

Air is the name given to a mixture of gases forming our atmosphere. In the main it is composed of Oxygen and Nitrogen, although other gases in very much smaller proportions are also present. It is of great importance to the quality of the finished weld that the two gases Oxygen and Nitrogen are excluded throughout the welding operation.

Oxygen combines more readily with molten metal than it would if the metal were at room temperature, and the degree of solubility increases rapidly as the temperature of the metal is raised above its melting point.

If Oxygen is allowed to come into contact with metal whilst it is at welding heat **metallic oxides** will certainly form. If these oxide formations remain along the grain boundaries intergranular weakness will be set up such as might give rise to cracking should any stress be placed upon the metal.

Nitrogen is a relatively chemically inert gas at normal temperature; but it will, under the influence of heat, combine with many metals to form nitrides. For example, Nitrogen will pass into solution in molten iron and upon cooling will eventually form a solid solution **iron nitride** which has a needle-like formation. These nitride needles are extremely hard and brittle, thus imparting these undesirable properties to the weld metal.

THE INERT GASES

Gas-shielded arc welding is only one of many modern industrial processes where the availability of an inert atmosphere allows reactive materials to be worked without contamination from the air.

These atmospheres are provided by a special group of gases comprising: ARGON, HELIUM, NEON, KRYPTON, and XENON, although only the first two are generally associated with welding.

Owing to their atomic stability gases of this type do not have active chemical properties of their own, but conform to one common characteristic, *i.e.* the property of inertness. Therefore they will not combine chemically with any other element whether it be in a solid, liquid or gaseous state.

GASES PRESENT IN THE ATMOSPHERE

GAS	PERCENTAGE
Nitrogen	78
Oxygen	21
Argon	0·9
Carbon Dioxide	0·03
Neon	0·0015
Helium	0·0015
Krypton	0·0001
Xenon	0·0001

QUESTIONS ON CHAPTER 2

(1) Which one of the following gases is removed by the process of REDUCTION:
  (a) Helium
  (b) Hydrogen
  (c) Oxygen
  (d) Nitrogen?

(2) The purpose of a gas-welding flux is to:
  (a) Lower the melting point of the metal
  (b) Lower the melting point of the oxide
  (c) Remove oxides from the surface of the metal
  (d) Remove elements from the parent metal.

(3) The flux coating of an electric arc electrode has a melting point:
  (a) Higher than the metallic core
  (b) Lower than the metallic core
  (c) The same as the metallic core
  (d) The same as the metal being welded.

(4) Which gas from the following will form a hard constituent when it combines with molten steel and remains after solidification has taken place:
  (a) Oxygen
  (b) Nitrogen
  (c) Hydrogen
  (d) Helium?

(5) Which one of the following gases is not present in the atmosphere:
  (a) Argon
  (b) Carbon dioxide
  (c) Hydrogen
  (d) Helium?

(Answers on page 100)

CHAPTER 3

Distortion and Stresses in Welding
The Effects of Distortion on Welded Structure
Types of Distortion—Factors Affecting Distortion
The Process of Stress Relieving

DISTORTION AND STRESSES IN WELDING

Metal subjected to a source of heat will increase in size due to expansion taking place throughout its mass. But if heat is applied to a small area only, the expansion will be local and uneven.

The surrounding metal which has remained comparatively cool will tend to prevent expansion of the heated metal and if the yield point of the metal has been reached during the heating cycle permanent deformation will take place. Consequently, the metal, upon cooling, will not return to its original form but will remain distorted.

The surrounding cold metal also offers resistance during cooling of the heated area and contractional stresses set up during plastic flow of the metal will also contribute to distortion.

The amount of distortion has a marked influence on the amount of structural strain that will remain in the metal after cooling.

As distortion increases, the strain will be much reduced which, again, is influenced by a reduction in plastic flow. But if any restraint is placed upon the metal to check distortion, **residual stresses** will remain after the metal has cooled and the final structure will be in a strained condition. This can often be remedied by the process of stress-relieving which will be discussed later.

Let us now consider the foregoing in connection with the welding of a metal.

Firstly, the amount of weld metal in comparison with the parent metal is relatively small; the greatest amount of heat is concentrated in this area as can be seen from Fig. 3.1. Secondly, the strength of the weld metal is greatly reduced at elevated temperatures, and being such a small mass in comparison with the structure as a whole will undertake most of the plastic flow during cooling. Under such conditions should the plastic flow exceed the metal's ultimate tensile strength resultant fracture may occur.

THE EFFECTS OF DISTORTION ON WELDED STRUCTURE

The relationship between welding and distortion can well be illustrated by the use of a flat plate which has had a slot cut along its length as shown in Fig. 3.2(a).

If a run of weld is now laid down along the top section the heat from the weld deposit will be transferred by conduction to the adjacent parent metal which will then have a tendency to expand in the direction shown in Fig. 3.2(b).

The bottom section of the plate being comparatively cool has no appreciable expansion at all, and being stronger than the heated area will resist any attempt to alter its shape. The top half must

18

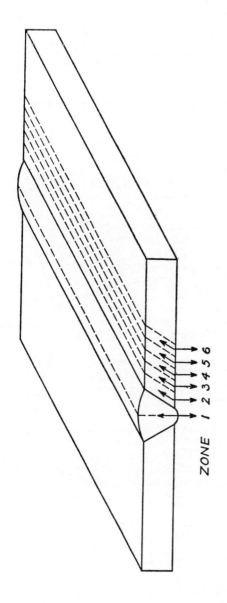

ZONE	APPROXIMATE TEMPERATURE °C
1	above 1500
2	1400 1500
3	900 1400
4	600 900
5	300 600
6	150 300

FIG. 3.1. TEMPERATURE GRADIENT IN THE WELDING ZONE

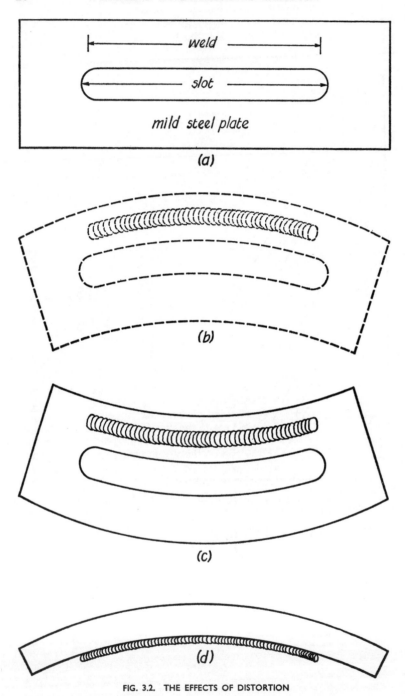

FIG. 3.2. THE EFFECTS OF DISTORTION

therefore absorb all the expansion by an increase in thickness at the expense of an increase in length. As the weld and parent metal have undergone expansion it is obvious that upon cooling both will contract, and resistance to this contraction will be set up by the bottom section of the plate. But as the weld and parent metal become colder their strength will again become greater and a point will be reached when the resistance of the bottom section will be overcome. Distortion of the plate will then take place in the opposite direction: Fig. 3.2(c).

In addition to the distortion already mentioned further distortion will take place on a different plane as is shown in Fig. 3.2(d). This is the result of unequal expansion between weld metal and surrounding plate which has tended to restrict movement upon heating and now cannot resist the contraction of the weld area as it becomes stronger upon cooling. Thus, a bowing of the plate is inevitable.

TYPES OF DISTORTION

The three types of distortion generally set up in welded structures are: **Angular distortion; Longitudinal distortion;** and **Transverse distortion.**

Angular distortion

Consider a single vee butt joint when the root run is laid down. The weld deposit has undergone expansion during the welding operation and is now contracting as it cools down. This shrinkage will draw the edges of the welded plates closer together, Fig. 3.3(a).

If a second run of weld is made the contractional pulling force is opposed by the now solid metal of the first run. The situation now arises where a force at the top of the vee is trying to pull the plate edges together and solid metal at the bottom is resisting this force [Fig. 3.3(b)] which gives rise to angular distortion along the joint.

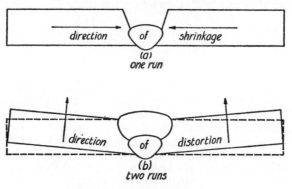

FIG. 3.3. ANGULAR DISTORTION

Longitudinal and Transverse distortion

These indicate the direction of distortion set up in the parent metal upon shrinkage of the weld metal.

Longitudinal distortion refers to bending which occurs along the length of the joint, and transverse distortion to that in a direction at right angles to the joint: Fig. 3.4.

FACTORS AFFECTING DISTORTION

If it were possible to preheat all structures and components before welding (thus obtaining an equal expansion between weld and parent metal and an equal contraction by controlled cooling after welding) no deformation would take place and there would be no distortion. But of course preheating is not always possible or practicable. Metals in a state of brittleness will fracture if any force due to unequal expansion and contraction is placed upon them. Therefore, preheating is necessary before welding commences and cooling should be at a governed rate after completion. Stresses that might cause fracture will not be set up if this procedure is adopted. [Cast-iron is a very good example of such a metal].

There are ways of reducing distortion without preheating such as the use of welding sequences which balance the forces set up by weld shrinkage. Skip welding and back stepping, Fig. 3.5(a)-(b), are two good examples.

Welding away from weld concentrations and using the shrinkage of one weld to counteract the shrinkage of another, as in the building up of a worn shaft, Fig. 3.6(a), or the welding of a double vee preparation, Fig. 3.6(b), are good welding practices.

The forces set up by shrinkage can be reduced by placing welds as near as possible to the neutral axis of a structure, so reducing the tendency of this force to pull the sections out of alignment.

It is very important to keep the heat input of any welding operation down to a minimum, for this is an effective means of minimizing shrinkage and, therefore, eliminating distortion.

CONCLUSION

The principal cause of distortion in welded assemblies is the physical law which governs the expansion and contraction of a metal. This distortion is aggravated by the degree of restraint put upon the weld and adjacent metal when subjected to drastic temperature gradients during welding operations, together with a severe reduction in strength at these elevated temperatures, thus having a marked effect on the metal's resistance to deformation.

The properties of elasticity and yield strength, as well as the coefficient of expansion of a metal, must be taken into consideration

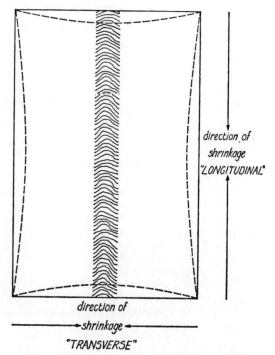

FIG. 3.4. LONGITUDINAL AND TRANSVERSE DISTORTION

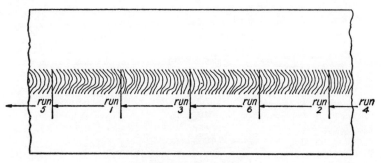

FIG. 3.5(a). SKIPWELDING

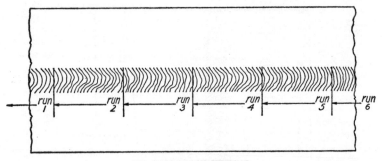

FIG. 3.5(b). BACK STEPPING

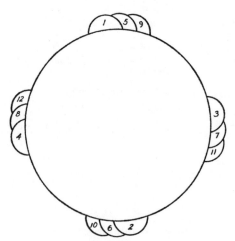

FIG. 3.6(a). RECLAIMING WORN SHAFT

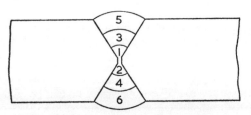

FIG. 3.6(b). DOUBLE VEE PREPARATION

when reviewing the problems of distortion in connection with welding design.

It is important to note that internal stresses can be introduced during manufacturing processes (such as cold rolling), and that when the metal is heated during welding the stresses are relieved, so causing distortion.

STRESS RELIEVING (POST-HEATING)

The magnitude of the stress remaining in a weldment is governed by the amount of distortion that has taken place; although stress is a prime factor in causing distortion it is greatly reduced as distortion increases.

It is always desirable to reduce the stress in a welded structure as much as possible; but at the same time it is essential that distortion should always be kept at a minimum and in many instances should be eliminated altogether. This can be made possible by restricting the movement of members of a structure during and after welding by the use of jigs and fixtures; but stress will remain and must be taken into consideration when assessing the structure's endurance during service.

In welded pressure vessels, for example, there is no distortion owing to the welding procedure normally used in such a fabrication (jigs, manipulators and welding sequence). However, stresses will remain after welding which must be removed before the pressure vessels go into service. Maximum strength under working conditions is made possible by the process of stress relieving.

THE PROCESS OF STRESS RELIEVING

The weldment to be stress-relieved is placed in a special furnace commonly known as a **stress-relieving oven,** and then heated up to a predetermined temperature. On reaching the required temperature cooling begins at a governed rate depending on the type of work and the conditions the component will have to undergo.

The range of temperature used in the relief of stress is normally below the recrystallization temperature; therefore stress can be removed without any great disturbance to the grain structure of the metal.

This method, however, cannot always be used to relieve stress. A welded pipe line, for example, could not be put into a furnace. In this case heat, sufficient to relieve the stress, is introduced into the weld and the adjacent parent metal by means of electrical induction coils. These coils can be contained in a thermal blanket which is wrapped around the parts to be heated (Fig. 3.7), or they are housed in a **clip-on muffle** as shown in Fig. 3.8. These electro-thermal blankets and muffles are of various sizes and can be connected to an alternating or direct current welding generator so that post-heating can be carried out on site. The temperature can accurately be

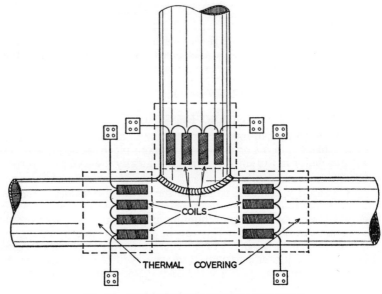

COILS

THERMAL COVERING

FIG. 3.7. STRESS RELIEVING BY INDUCTION COILS

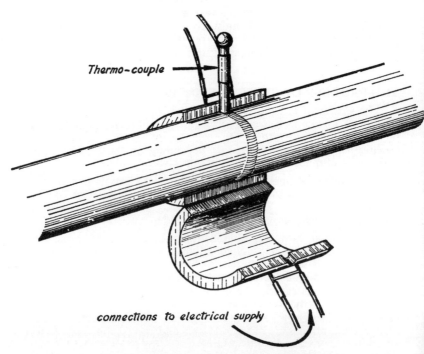

Thermo-couple

connections to electrical supply

FIG. 3.8. ELECTRO-THERMAL STRESS-RELIEVING MUFFLE

determined by means of a thermo-couple (see Appendix, page 95) connected to the heating system. Cooling of the work can be controlled by a reduction in the electrical input, or by removing part of the asbestos covering if the induction coils themselves do not form part of the blanket.

THE EFFECTS OF DISTORTION ON PIPEWORK

The joining of hollow section in the form of tube and pipe produces special problems of distortion due to their geometrical form.

The transverse shrinkage in an end-to-end butt weld will cause a reduction in the overall length of the pipes being joined and this reduction would have to be taken into consideration when designing pipe runs. On the other hand longitudinal shrinkage of the weld would be negligible and could therefore be ignored.

Angular distortion is usually limited to pipe flanges and can be eliminated by pre-setting or by welding flanges back-to-back in pairs.

Bowing is another type of distortion associated with welded pipework, the main problem being the welding of branches where it is seldom possible to balance heat input. Longitudinal shrinkage of the weld will therefore contribute to the bowing of the main pipe.

QUESTIONS ON CHAPTER 3

(1) The shrinkage that takes place at right angles to the line of a welded joint is termed:
   - (a)   Angular
   - (b)   Transverse
   - (c)   Longitudinal
   - (d)   Latitudinal.

(2) Which one of the following would help to reduce distortion:
   - (a)   Concentration of welding to one area
   - (b)   Increasing the input of welding heat
   - (c)   Use of single vee preparation
   - (d)   Use of welding sequences?

(3) Which one of the following statements is incorret:
   - (a)   The greater the distortion the less residual stress
   - (b)   The greater the distortion the greater the residual stress
   - (c)   The greater the restraint the greater the residual stress
   - (d)   The greater the weld concentration the greater the residual stress?

(4) Is the range of temperature used in the relief of stress:
   - (a)   Below the recrystallization temperature
   - (b)   Above the recrystallization temperature
   - (c)   At the recrystallization temperature
   - (d)   At the solidification temperature?

(5) The overall length of a pipe line can be affected by:
   - (a)   Transverse shrinkage
   - (b)   Longitudinal shrinkage
   - (c)   Angular shrinkage
   - (d)   Circumferential shrinkage.

(Answers on page 100)

CHAPTER 4

Mechanical Properties of Metals—Stress and Deformation
Strain and Elasticity——Stress/Strain Curves——Proof Stress—
Fatigue

MECHANICAL PROPERTIES OF METALS

The behaviour of metals under working conditions is greatly influenced by the mechanical properties possessed by the metals themselves.

These properties are as follows:

(i) Ductility

This property enables a metal to be stretched lengthwise, and can be defined as the ability to be drawn into wire. The ductility of a metal is determined by the amount it will increase in length before it finally becomes brittle and fails.

Ductility is greatly reduced upon an increase in temperature of the metal itself. Thus, in the manufacture of wire the metal is usually drawn cold, giving it greater ductility.

(ii) Malleability

Many metals possess this property which allows them to be flattened under compression without rupture, such as in forging or rolling operations.

Most metals have a greater malleability when worked in their hot state, which is advantageous as less power is then needed during the deformation of the metal.

(iii) Plasticity

Plasticity is essential in a metal if it is to be used in any forming process, as it is the ability of that metal to be worked into any given shape without fracture.

Few metals are plastic when cold. An application of heat during most forming processes will enhance plasticity, although there are exceptions where an increase in temperature may induce brittleness into the metal.

(iv) Brittleness

This term signifies a lack of plasticity in a metal. Resultant fracture without any appreciable deformation is usual when a brittle metal is subjected to a fairly large impact. (This is a common occurrence with many metals in their cast state).

In some circumstances brittleness in a metal can be reduced by the application of heat; but, as already mentioned, heat can also produce brittleness.

(v) Hardness

Hardness in a metal can produce a resistance to indentation or abrasion. The measurement of hardness is usally based upon a metal's resistance to indentation, although tests can be devised to determine the metal's resistance to wear from abrasion.

Hardness is normally introduced into a metal as a result of deformation during cold working. This is known as **work hardening** and will cause an increase in strength at the expense of ductility.

When an alloy is formed by the mixing of two or more pure metals, the resultant hardness of the alloy is far greater than the individual hardness of the metals themselves.

In many ferrous alloys extreme hardness can be produced by raising the alloy to a high temperature, followed by rapid cooling.

Other special alloys will even become harder with age after heat treatment. This is known as age or precipitation hardening and is described in the section on THE WELDING OF ALUMINIUM ALLOYS, page 76.

The Brinell Hardness Test

In this test a hardened steel ball is pressed into the surface of the specimen by the application of a standard load for a set period of time.

The indentation formed by the ball is then measured with the aid of a special microscope and the Brinell hardness number H is calculated by dividing the applied load by the area of indentation:

$$H = \frac{\text{Load in kg}}{\text{Area of indentation in sq mm}}$$

The diameter of the ball is usually 10 mm and the applied load 3000 kg. This load can vary for certain metals, *e.g.* steels 3000 kg, copper 1000 kg, and aluminium 500 kg.

The Diamond Hardness Test

Although the Brinell machine is used extensively in the testing of many metals and alloys there is a limit to the range of hardness values that it can produce, for if too hard a material is tested by this method inaccurate readings can result. These are due to deformation or flattening of the steel ball when in contact with the harder surface and, therefore, a low hardness figure will be attained.

To eliminate this effect there are various types of testing machines which utilize diamond indentors instead of a steel ball.

The diamond indentor may be pryamid-shaped as in the Vickers testing machine; or in the form of a cone as in the Rockwell testing machine. The resultant hardness values produced are expressed as follows:

Vickers pyramid number (V.P.N.)
Rockwell hardness number.

It is important to remember that hardness numbers become higher as the materials being tested become harder.

STRESS AND DEFORMATION

When a metal in service comes under a load, it will have a tendency to deform in the direction of that load.

If the load produces elongation in the metal with a reduction in cross-section, then the load has subjected the metal to a **tensile stress** as illustrated in Fig. 4.1.

FIG. 4.1.   TENSILE STRESS

If the direction of load is reversed (as in Fig. 4.2) the metal will then be placed under a **compressive stress** giving rise to an increase in cross-section.

FIG. 4.2.   COMPRESSIVE STRESS

Another type of simple stress is called **shear stress.** This is set up when a metal undertakes loads which are not in the same line of force, but generally act at right angles to the cross-section of the metal in opposite directions. This can be explained as the sliding of one plane across an adjacent plane as shown in Fig. 4.3.

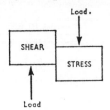

FIG. 4.3.   SHEAR STRESS

Welded and riveted structures (see Fig. 4.4) are often placed in this class of stress, which sometimes can be found in association with tensile and compressive stresses.

STRAIN AND ELASTICITY

If the loading of a metal does produce a dimensional change, then a state of **strain** will be set up in that metal although the change of dimension may be imperceptible.

Most metals, however, possess a very important property known as **elasticity** which will enable the metal to regain its original dimensions and cause the disappearance of strain when the load is removed. This regaining of original shape is only possible provided the magnitude of load has not caused deformation beyond the elastic limit of the metal under stress.

As long as the extension of the metal is within its elastic limit,

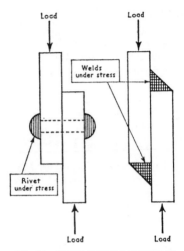

FIG. 4.4. SHEAR STRESS ILLUSTRATED

the strain set up will be directly proportional to the stress producing the strain.

The sum of elasticity possessed by the metal can be calculated by a physical constant known as the **modulus of elasticity.** This modulus, which indicates the degree of rigidity possessed by the metal, is of great importance in structural work, especially in the design of beams.

Beyond the elastic limit, however, the strain will begin to increase more rapidly than the stress until a point is reached when the proportion of the strain is so much in excess of the stress that a breakdown will occur in the metal.

STRESS/STRAIN CURVES

If a metal specimen is placed under tensile stress because of an increasing load until the breaking point of the metal does occur, it will pass through certain phases which can be determined and shown by the plotting of a stress/strain curve. This curve is obtained by taking a series of load and extension readings and plotting stress against strain.

To understand the various physical changes which will take place, the stress/strain curve produced when normalized low carbon steel is placed under an increasing load is illustrated in Fig. 4.5. Each part of this particular curve will be dealt with separately.

The first section of the curve which will be seen as the straight line *OP* is often called the **line of proportionality,** for in this region if the extension (strain) is proportional to the applied load (stress) the metal has obeyed Hooke's law. Thus, if the stress increases by 50 per cent the strain will also increase by 50 per cent, thereby producing a straight line indicating the elastic range of the material.

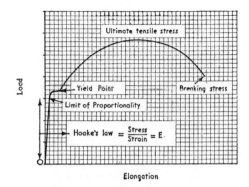

FIG. 4.5.   STRESS/STRAIN CURVE FOR LOW CARBON STEEL

$$\text{Stress} = \frac{\text{load}}{\text{cross-sectional area}}$$

$$\text{Strain} = \frac{\text{extension of gauge length}}{\text{original gauge length}}$$

$$\text{Hooke's Law} = \frac{\text{Stress}}{\text{Strain}} = E \text{ (kN/mm}^2\text{)}$$

E is a constant known as Young's Modulus.

The curve now begins to deviate from the straight line, and the strain ceases to be proportional to the stress.

If the load is now removed the metal will not return to its original dimensions but will take on permanent set.

This point on the curve, known as **the limit of proportionality**, will mark the end of elastic deformation, and the beginning of plastic deformation. Thus, it serves as an indication as to the maximum load the metal will withstand without exhibiting permanent extension.

Just beyond the limit of proportionality it will be noted that the curve changes abruptly.

Here the metal has undergone a marked increase in extension although an increase of load has not been registered.

The point on the curve where this sudden yielding of the metal without additional load takes place is termed **the yield point** and is of great importance when assessing the strength of the particular metal specimen under observation.

Yield Point Stress

To calculate the strength of the metal at its yield point, the yield load is divided by the original cross-sectional area of that metal.

As the applied load continues to become greater an increase in the strength of the metal will be evident, due to the direct result of work hardening during plastic deformation.

The curve will gradually rise as the metal becomes more rigid until a peak is reached denoting the maximum stress the metal will endure. Hence it shows ultimate tensile strength.

To calculate the ultimate tensile strength (U.T.S.) of the metal, the maximum load indicated on the stress/strain curve is divided by the original cross-sectional area.

Although the metal up to this point has had a uniform reduction in its cross-sectional area, there will now be a rapid decrease in a concentrated area that has been unable to work harden quickly enough to counteract the effect of the increased load.

Therefore the specimen will suffer necking as shown in Fig. 4.6.

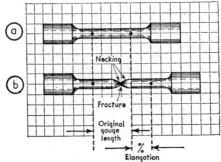

FIG. 4.6. (a) METAL SPECIMEN BEFORE LOADING AND
(b) AFTER LOADING

The curve will now begin to drop as the load required to stretch the metal will become less and will end when fracture eventually takes place at the smallest cross-section in the neck of the specimen.

Elongation

If the metal specimen has had a predetermined distance marked off along its length before being placed under load, then the elongation can be calculated by measuring the extension produced up to ultimate fracture, and expressing this sum as a percentage of the original gauge length. This percentage serves as an accurate account of the ductility of the metal.

Another value of ductility can be indicated by the reduction in cross-sectional area of the specimen which has taken place during loading to breaking point. This reduction is also expressed as a percentage, after a comparison by measurement has been made between the original and final cross-sectional areas of the specimen at the point of fracture.

The Relationship between Hardness, Strength and Ductility

If we now compare a stress/strain curve produced by a harder steel, *e.g.* **high carbon steel** (Fig. 4.7) with the curve for the softer low carbon steel it will be seen that certain changes have taken place.

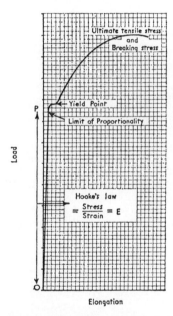

FIG. 4.7. STRESS/STRAIN CURVE FOR HIGH CARBON STEEL

There is, for instance, a longer line of proportionality in respect of the high carbon steel which signifies a greater elasticity than that possessed by the low carbon steel, although the cross-sectional areas of both specimens are identical.

It will be noted that the yield point load for the harder steel has been recorded at a much higher level than the corresponding point on the curve for the low carbon specimen. But the most important factor may be observed at the apex of the curve denoting the ultimate tensile strength of the high carbon steel. Although the metal at this point has undergone a much greater load than the previous specimen, the elongation has been reduced to such an extent that the tensile stress and breaking stress have now occurred at the same instant on the stress/strain curve.

The following table will help to form a comparison between the two steels.

TYPE OF STEEL	YIELD STRENGTH N/mm²	TENSILE STRENGTH N/mm²	ELONGATION PERCENTAGE	HARDNESS BRINELL
Low carbon	247	432	30	150
High carbon	695	926	10	450

This comparison indicates that an **increase in hardness** will normally produce a **greater tensile strength,** but invariably brings about a **reduction in ductility.**

PROOF STRESS

As already stated, the position of the yield point on a stress/strain curve is of great importance when estimating the strength of a material.

Unfortunately, most non-ferrous metals and alloys (together with certain high-tensile steels) do not exhibit a well-defined yield point when placed under a tensile load, therefore a measure of comparison known as **proof stress** is used to determine the tenacity of such materials.

The proof stress will correspond to a pre-established permanent set which is usually 0·1 per cent of the original gauge length denoted by A on the stress/strain curve in Fig. 4.8.

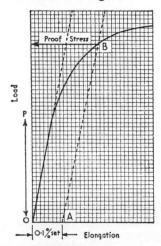

FIG 4.8. DETERMINATION OF PROOF STRESS

FATIGUE

When a metal is subjected to a fluctuating load a condition of cyclic stressing is set up which eventually can result in a complete structural breakdown.

When this progressive failure does take place under many repetitions of a load it is recognized as **fatigue failure** which probably has originated from a local region of structural weakness.

This weakness in welded joints can be due to internal defects in the form of cracks, porosity or non-metallic inclusions from which the line of failure has progressed gradually until ultimate breakdown has occurred.

The fatigue strength of a weldment can be greatly affected when stress concentration is set up due to bad joint design, notches or abrupt change of section which can be the case if excessive weld reinforcement is evident.

Surface defects such as discontinuities in penetration, lack of fusion and undercutting will also have an influence upon the resistance of the weld metal to fatigue failure and for this reason should never be tolerated under any circumstances.

QUESTIONS ON CHAPTER 4

(1) When a longitudinal load is put upon a lap joint the stress set up is normally:

    (a) Shear stress
    (b) Tensile stress
    (c) Compressive stress
    (d) Residual stress.

(2) When a metal regains its original shape when a stress acting upon it is removed, the metal is said to have:

    (a) Ductility
    (b) Plasticity
    (c) Malleability
    (d) Elasticity.

(3) Percentage elongation of a metal undergoing a tensile test is a measure of:

    (a) Elasticity
    (b) Plasticity
    (c) Ductility
    (d) Malleability.

(4) Proof stress is used when non-ferrous metals are undergoing tensile tests to determine the amount of:

    (a) Tenacity
    (b) Elasticity
    (c) Plasticity
    (d) Ductility.

(5) When a metal is subjected to a fluctuating load a condition of cyclic stressing can be set up which eventually can result in structural breakdown known as:

    (a) Tensile failure
    (b) Fatigue failure
    (c) Yield failure
    (d) Shear failure.

(Answers on page 100)

CHAPTER 5

Cold Working and its Effects on the Structure and Mechanical Properties of Metals
The Process of Cold Working and Annealing
Hot Working and its Effect on the Structure and Mechanical Properties of Metals
The Process of Normalizing

COLD WORKING AND ITS EFFECTS ON THE STRUCTURE AND MECHANICAL PROPERTIES OF METALS

When a ductile metal comes under stress it will deform in the direction of that stress. If the applied stress is not sufficient to produce deformation beyond the elastic limit of the metal it will regain its original shape when the stress acting upon it is removed. This type of deformation is termed **elastic deformation** and is illustrated in a simple manner in Fig. 5.1.

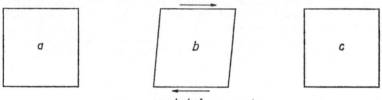

a   crystal before stressing
b   crystal during stressing
c   crystal after stressing

FIG. 5.1.   ELASTIC DEFORMATION

If, however, the stress put upon the metal is so severe as to set up deformation beyond the elastic limit then the metal will remain permanently deformed when the stress is removed. This is **plastic deformation** and is illustrated in Fig. 5.2. Plastic deformation is due to a phenomenon known as **slip**. This refers to planes of atoms in a crystal sliding over each other so that the crystal will eventually

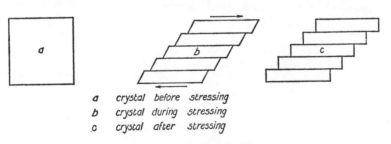

a   crystal before stressing
b   crystal during stressing
c   crystal after stressing

FIG. 5.2.   PLASTIC DEFORMATION

39

become permanently distorted. As slip progresses in one plane it will reach a point where resistance to further slip develops in that plane and will begin in an adjacent parallel plane, continuing until all the planes in the crystal have undergone their maximum slipping motion. When the crystal has completed its deformation in this way it will exert pressure upon adjacent crystals and initiate slip in those crystals which have their planes in favourable positions. This process of slip can eventually affect all the crystals throughout the structure of the metal, at which stage the metal will have reached its limit of plastic deformation. Further applied stress would now create a complete breakdown within the crystal structure and resultant fracture would occur.

It is found that some metals are more liable to plastic deformation by slip than others, due to the particular atomic formation existing within the metallic crystal itself. To show the influence that atomic structures have upon the mechanical properties of metals consider the contrast between gold and zinc. Gold has a simple face-centred cubic lattice (Fig. 5.3), giving great malleability and ductility to the metal. Zinc, with its complicated hexagonal close-packed lattice (Fig. 5.4) produces a marked reduction in malleability and ductility. As plastic deformation increases owing to slip so the metal itself becomes progressively harder. Many theories have been put forward as to why this happens, but as they involve complicated metallurgical study they will not be dealt with in this book. The foregoing explanation of slip has been simplified to give only a general idea.

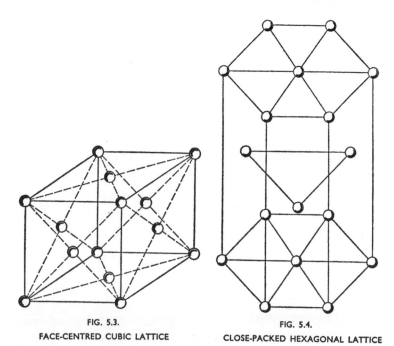

FIG. 5.3.
FACE-CENTRED CUBIC LATTICE

FIG. 5.4.
CLOSE-PACKED HEXAGONAL LATTICE

THE PROCESS OF COLD WORKING AND ANNEALING

The working of a metal by such means as bending, rolling, hammering, drawing, etc., when below the recrystallization temperature is termed **cold working.** During this process the metal undergoes a progressive hardening known as **work hardening,** resulting in an increase in tensile strength coupled with a reduction in ductility. Cold working is generally applied at the final stages of production to enable more accurate dimensions to be obtained and to give a clean smooth finish to the material. Hardness as required can be produced by an accurate amount of cold work being carried out during manufacture of products made from metallic alloys that cannot be hardened by other means.

The crystals of a cold worked metal will be distorted and greatly elongated in the direction of the cold work, thus producing a crystalline structure of a fibrous nature. Strain hardening of the metal will become evident and resultant stresses that could contribute to brittle fracture during service can be set up if the process of cold working is much prolonged. After a certain amount of cold work has been carried out upon a metal the undesirable structure formed will have to be modified before continuing the cold working. This is made possible by heat treatment in the form of **annealing** during which the metal is heated in a furnace to a prescribed temperature* and then allowed to cool at a governed rate whilst still in the furnace. This treatment will soften the metal and will remove internal stresses set up by cold working, and also form a finer undistorted grain due to recrystallization within the structure of the metal. Ductility is improved and cold working can be continued until annealing is again evident.   Some metals, such as lead and tin, will recrystallize at room temperature. Recrystallization then takes place simultaneously with the deformation of the crystal grains. Therefore, these metals will not work harden during any cold working process.

During recrystallization of a cold-worked metal, grain growth can occur unless a rigid control is kept upon temperature and time. Grain growth can be caused by excessive heating of the metal to a temperature well above its recrystallization point; or to a too slow cooling rate after recrystallization has taken place. In both cases a very coarse granular structure will be apparent.

Enlarged crystal grains will cause a decrease in the ductility and tensile strength of a metal; but these properties will be enhanced when normal grain size in the form of equi-axed crystals have once again been restored by further recrystallization.

[Cold-worked crystal grains, recrystallization, equi-axed crystal grains, and grain growth are all shown in Fig. 5.5].

HOT WORKING AND ITS EFFECTS ON THE STRUCTURE AND MECHANICAL PROPERTIES OF METALS

One of the most important metallurgical aspects of any hot working process is the fact that deformation and recrystallization will take place simultaneously so long as the operation is carried

* See Critical Temperatures, page 54.

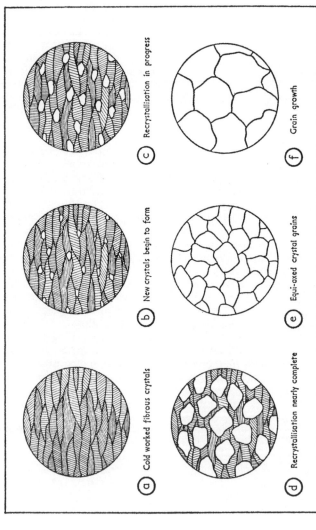

(a) Cold worked fibrous crystals

(b) New crystals begin to form

(c) Recrystallisation in progress

(d) Recrystallisation nearly complete

(e) Equi-axed crystal grains

(f) Grain growth

FIG. 5.5. COLD-WORKED CRYSTAL GRAINS, RECRYSTALLIZATION, EQUI-AXED CRYSTAL GRAINS, AND GRAIN GROWTH

out in its entirety above the recrystallization temperature of the metal.

The main advantage of hot working is that a considerable speeding-up of the process will be possible owing to the absence of inter-stage annealing—a treatment necessary during any cold deformation process.

Another advantage that hot working has is that far less power is needed to produce deformation, for mechanical properties such as malleability and plasticity are greatly improved when metals and alloys are subjected to heat. There are few exceptions to the rule that an increase in temperature may induce brittleness into a metal although there are alloys that can only be hot worked owing to their extreme hardness or brittleness when cold.

The important factor in any hot working process is the finishing temperature, which should be just above the recrystallization temperature of the metal, giving a fine-grained crystal structure in the finished product.

If the finishing temperature is too high the crystal grains will become enlarged and **grain growth** will be evident. If the finishing temperature is below the recrystallization temperature the crystal grains will be distorted (as in cold working) with resultant work hardening.

The advantages of hot working can be summarized as an operational speeding up with less power than that required in cold deformation. Nevertheless there are disadvantages such as (a) an inferior surface condition can be produced due to oxide scale being rolled or hammered into the metal during the shaping operation; and (b) inability to produce accurate finishing dimensions.

[After the hot rolling of some steels their final size and shape are brought about by cold work. This produces a smooth bright finish to the metal's surface; there is also a greater control over the final dimensions. The tensile strength of the cold worked steel will be increased owing to the process of work hardening].

Fig. 5.6(a) and (b) show two processes used in the shaping of metals: **rolling** and **forging.**

THE PROCESS OF NORMALIZING

This process resembles the annealing process (already explained in connection with cold working) since the prescribed temperature for both processes is the same.* The difference lies in the method of cooling. In the normalizing process the metal is removed from the furnace and allowed to cool down in still air at ordinary temperature. In the annealing process the metal remains in the furnace excluded of air until reaching room temperature. The cooling rate is much faster in normalizing; therefore the structure of the metal† will be modified to give greater tensile strength, hardness, and toughness whilst the ductility will not be greatly affected. Normalizing will relieve stress produced by work and will restore the structure to one

---

* See Critical Temperatures, page 54.
† See Sorbitic Structure, page 53.

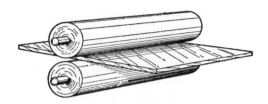

FIG. 5.6(a). THE PROCESS OF ROLLING USED IN THE SHAPING OF METALS

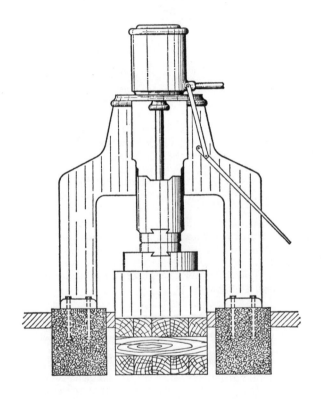

FIG. 5.6(b). THE PROCESS OF FORGING USED IN THE SHAPING OF METALS

having a small grain size if grain growth has taken place due to over-heating or over-annealling.

Normalizing is often the final treatment in the processing of steel to bring about with greater accuracy the properties of tensile strength, hardness, etc. to the required specifications.

QUESTIONS ON CHAPTER 5

(1) When a steel undergoes a COLD WORKED process it becomes progressively:
   (a) Softer
   (b) Harder
   (c) Ductile
   (d) Malleable.

(2) When a cold-worked metal is heated up to its recrystallization temperature it becomes:
   (a) Harder
   (b) Softer
   (c) Stays unchanged in hardness
   (d) Stays unchanged in softness.

(3) The process of hot working is always carried out:
   (a) Above the metal's recrystallization temperature
   (b) Below the metal's recrystallization temperature
   (c) At the metal's recrystallization temperature
   (d) At the metal's solidification temperature.

(4) When a steel is heated in a furnace and then cooled in air at ordinary temperature the process is one of:
   (a) Annealing
   (b) Hardening
   (c) Normalizing
   (d) Tempering.

(5) Which one of the following structures is predominant in a normalized steel:
   (a) Troostite
   (b) Bainite
   (c) Sorbite
   (d) Martensite?

(Answers on page 100)

CHAPTER 6

The Chemical Composition of Plain Carbon Steel
Alloy Steels——The Effect of Carbon on Iron
The Effect of Heat on the Structure of Steel
The Effect on Steel of Various Cooling and Reheating Rates
Hardening and Tempering
The Critical Range in Plain Carbon Steels

THE CHEMICAL COMPOSITION OF PLAIN CARBON STEEL

Steel is the most versatile of all industrial materials. It is produced in many forms and compositions all of which are predominant in iron and carbon; other elements are introduced intentionally or unavoidably into the metal during manufacture.

The structural characteristics and mechanical properites of steel can be greatly influenced by the ratio of carbon to iron contained in the alloy, and by the contrasting effects that other elements such as silicon, manganese, phosphorus and sulphur have upon the metal.

It is therefore necessary to understand the action that each of these elements has upon the chemical and physical properties of steel.

Carbon

Carbon has the greatest influence on the mechanical properties of steel. As the percentage of carbon is increased so the tensile strength, toughness and hardness of the steel increase, with a marked reduction in ductility. Carbon occurs in steel in the combined state with iron as **iron carbide** and it is due to this that a wide range in the physical properties of steel is possible by means of heat treatment.

Silicon

Silicon is particularly useful during the manufacturing processes of steel because of its deoxidizing effect upon the metal. The silicon remaining in the finished steel is dissolved in the iron and has no appreciable effect upon the physical properties of the steel itself.

Manganese

During the steel-making process manganese is used as a **reducing agent.** This action brings about the combination of manganese with the oxides of the molten metal thus forming **manganese oxide** which collects in the slag. Also, manganese combines with sulphur and thereby decreases the harmful effect that sulphur has upon steel.

Phosphorus

Phosphorus is an impurity in steel and combines with iron to form a compound which is present in solution in the metal. A high phosphorus content causes failure in steel when subjected to cold-working. This condition is known as **cold shortness.**

Sulphur

Sulphur is another impurity in steel and occurs in the structure as **iron sulphide** or as **manganese sulphide**. As iron sulphide it forms at the grain boundaries of the steel and, having a low melting point, causes a lack of cohesion between the grains of the metal when it is subjected to hot-working. This is a condition known as **hot shortness**. Manganese sulphide has a higher melting point than iron sulphide so it does not liquefy at the temperatures used in hot-working processes. It is therefore less harmful to the structure of steel than the compound iron sulphide.

N.B.: It is obvious that high quality steels will contain less phosphorus and sulphur than steels of poor quality, which have been manufactured to low specification.

See Appendix 1 (page 89) for typical compositions and applications of plain carbon steels.

ALLOY STEELS

If certain alloying elements are added to plain carbon steels during their manufacture the quality of the steel produced will be much improved. Also, there will be a marked improvement in the physical and mechanical properties even without the use of thermal treatment.

Steels which undergo this special processing belong to a very important group known as **alloy steels**. Whereas the properties of plain carbon steels are related directly to the amount of carbon in their structure, the properties of these alloy steels are solely dependent upon the presence of additional elements. These elements may generally be found either in solution with iron or as a compound with carbon; they can be separate entities in the composition of the alloy steel or used in conjunction with each other when the highest quality is desired. Examples illustrating formation and combination of elements in alloy steel can be shown, for instance, by the addition of nickel to steel which, after going into solution with the iron, has a profound strengthening effect upon the metal; and the increase in hardenability of steel brought about by the addition of chromium which forms a compound with carbon. Nickel steels are noted for their high strength and toughness: chromium steels produce varying degrees of hardness to the metal. Therefore, alloy steels containing both nickel and chromium will possess a combination of all the above properties. When sufficient amounts of nickel and chromium are added to plain carbon steels a very important group of ferrous alloys, **stainless steels,** are formed which are not only high strength steels but also corrosion resistant. Other metallic elements used in the production of alloy steels which embrace the **low alloy structural steels** and the **high alloy tool steels** are as follows.

Manganese

Manganese is added to ordinary steels for the purpose of combining with sulphur and preventing hot shortness. It is also added in greater quantities to form work-hardening alloys, **manganese**

steels, when an increase in hardness and a resistance to wear during service is required.

Nickel
Although nickel greatly increases the strength of steel there is no appreciable decrease in the metal's ductility—hence the suitability of this material for constructional purposes. There is also granular refinement in steel due to the presence of nickel in the structure.

Nickel is found in most low alloy structural steels and in special nickel steels which are subject to very low temperatures during service.

Chromium
The addition of chromium to steel does not appreciably lower ductility even when the hardness and tensile strength are greatly increased.

A serious disadvantage of alloying chromium to steel is the chromium's tendency to promote excessive grain growth during the heating cycle of the material, particularly if overheating is evident, or prolonged heating is carried out during normal heat-treatment. Another serious disadvantage is that chromium steels can be susceptible to temper brittleness if slowly cooled through various heat ranges from previous tempering temperatures; but with the introduction of other alloying elements grain growth and temper brittleness can be greatly modified.

Chromium is to be found in most structural and heat-resisting alloy steels.

N.B.: Manganese and nickel will lower the critical points in steel. Chromium has the opposite effect on steel and raises the critical points. For critical points of steel see page 54.

Molybdenum
Molybdenum, like chromium, will increase hardenability in steel; but its advantage over chromium is that it has a marked effect in reducing temper brittleness. Molybdenum will also raise the temperature at which grain growth normally takes place in plain carbon steels.

In solid solution molybdenum produces greater strength and toughness in the steel and improves resistance to creep at elevated temperatures, which is the reason for molybdenum-bearing steels being used extensively in high temperature work.

Vanadium
This will combine with carbon to form a carbide which has a beneficial effect on the mechanical properties of heat-treated steels: even small quantities have an appreciable effect upon hardenability and can induce secondary hardening into high-speed steels.

Vanadium raises the temperature at which grain growth normally takes place in plain carbon steels and is an active grain refiner as well as an excellent deoxidant.

When chromium is added to vanadium steels the very important group of chrom-vanadium alloy steels is formed.

Cobalt

This is one of the very few alloying elements that will reduce hardness in steel. It raises the tempering temperature which can be of great importance in producing certain types of high-speed tool steel. It is used in large proportions in the manufacture of magnet steels.

Tungsten

Tungsten forms a strong hard carbide when alloyed with steel, producing a desirable strengthening of the metal over an extensive range of temperature. It will increase the ability of steel to remain hard and to resist tempering up to relatively high temperatures, which makes it a suitable alloying agent in high-speed steel. Tungsten will reduce decarburization during the hot working of steel and has a considerable effect on grain refinement.

Tungsten is used as a single alloying element only in a few specialized steels; it is more likely to be found in combination with other metals forming larger groups of ferrous alloys.

THE EFFECT OF CARBON ON IRON

The atomic arrangement of iron at ordinary temperature is in the form of a body-centred cubic lattice (Fig. 6.1) and when this particular geometrical structure is present only a minute quantity of carbon will be taken into solution with the iron.

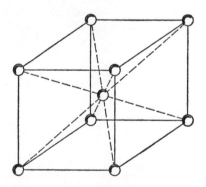

FIG. 6.1. BODY-CENTRED CUBIC LATTICE

Apart from this negligible amount of carbon in solution the rest of the carbon present in any steel combines with iron to form an extremely hard compound, **iron carbide.**

Therefore, the two main constituents of steel comprise a solid solution of carbon in iron known as **ferrite**; and a compound of iron and carbon forming iron carbide or **cementite.**

When there is 0·83 per cent carbon present in steel the whole mass will consist entirely of alternate layers of **ferrite** and **cementite** and this laminated structure has the name of **pearlite**: Fig. 6.2. This particular steel is known as an **eutectoid steel** because its composition

MICROSTRUCTURE

FIG. 6.2. THE PEARLITIC STRUCTURE OF AN EUTECTOID STEEL (0·83% CARBON)

corresponds to the eutectoid point on the iron/carbon equilibrium diagram: see Fig. 6.9, page 55.

Steels containing less than 0·83 per cent carbon are known as **hypoeutectoid steels** and are made up of varying amounts of **ferrite** and **pearlite**: Fig. 6.3.

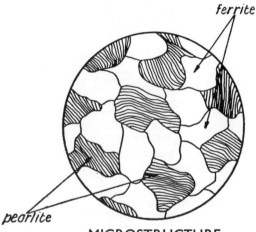

ferrite

FIG. 6.3.
THE FERRITE/PEARLITE STRUCTURE OF A HYPOEUTECTOID STEEL (LESS THAN 0·83% CARBON)

pearlite

MICROSTRUCTURE

Steels having a higher carbon content than 0·83 per cent are known as **hypereutectoid steels** and consist of **pearlite** with an excess of **cementite** forming on the grain-boundaries: Fig. 6.4. In hypoeutectoid steels **ferrite** contributes to the metal's relative softness and ductility, whilst in hypereutectoid steels **cementite** produces hardness and brittleness.

THE EFFECT OF HEAT ON THE STRUCTURE OF STEEL

Although iron has a body-centred cubic lattice at normal temperature it will undergo an allotropic change when heated—namely,

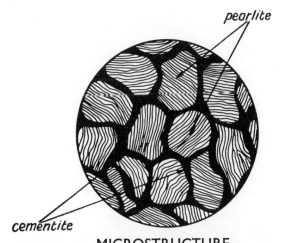

pearlite

cementite

MICROSTRUCTURE

FIG. 6.4.   THE PEARLITE/CEMENTITE STRUCTURE OF A HYPEREUTECTOID STEEL
(MORE THAN 0·83% CARBON)

a rearrangement of atoms and thus a new geometrical pattern in the form of a face-centred cubic lattice: Fig. 5.3, page 40.

This new atomic arrangement will allow the iron to take into solution a much greater amount of carbon than was possible before.

When steel passes through certain ranges of temperature the same transformation of iron will take place within its structure. Therefore, under these conditions the iron will be able to dissolve the carbon which is present in the steel as iron carbide. As the absorption of carbon progresses, a gradual breaking down of the iron carbide will occur, leaving uncombined iron in the structure which transforms and dissolves more carbon from the remaining iron carbide.

This process will be continuous with a constant rise in temperature until all the carbon present in the steel has passed into solution with the iron to produce a new structure called **austenite**: Fig. 6.5.

FIG. 6.5.   AUSTENITE. A SOLID SOLUTION
OF CARBON IN FACE-CENTRED IRON.
THIS STRUCTURE IS NOT RETAINED IN
ORDINARY QUENCHED STEEL, BUT WITH
THE ADDITION OF HIGH PERCENTAGES
OF MANGANESE OR NICKEL THE ALLOY
STEELS FORMED WILL REMAIN
AUSTENITIC AT NORMAL TEMPERATURE

MICROSTRUCTURE

If the heated steel is now allowed to cool down slowly the reverse of the heating process will take place. The face-centred cubic iron will begin to revert to its original body-centred cubic structure; as this atomic change proceeds, the dissolved carbon will separate out from the iron. This precipitated carbon will now combine with the newly-formed free iron to produce once again the compound iron carbide or **cementite.**

THE EFFECT ON STEEL OF VARIOUS COOLING AND REHEATING RATES

If the steel is cooled down at a very fast rate (quenching in water), from its austenitic condition the iron will still undergo atomic change, but the dissolved carbon which is in solution with iron will not have enough time to separate out. Therefore, most of the carbon will remain in a super-saturated state within the body-centred cubic iron itself. This will cause an unstable condition to take place throughout the entire structure of the steel and will give rise to a hard, brittle constituent consisting of an acicular structure, known as **martensite:** Fig. 6.6. Modifications to this undesirable structure

MICROSTRUCTURE

FIG. 6.6.
MARTENSITE. NEEDLE-LIKE CRYSTALS IN ANGULAR ARRANGEMENT. THIS STRUCTURE IS FOUND IN RAPIDLY-COOLED STEEL, ALTHOUGH THE LOWER THE CARBON CONTENT OF THE STEEL THE MORE RAPID MUST BE THE COOLING IN ORDER TO RETAIN MARTENSITE

can be done by reheating the steel so that more carbon will be allowed to separate out from the solid solution and unite with free iron to form a more balanced structure.

Granular refinement is one of the first desirable effects to take place upon a reapplication of heat. The new structure to be formed is called **troostite** (Fig. 6.7), which is not quite so hard as martensite but has greater toughness.

[This granular troostite is sometimes called **secondary troostite** to distinguish it from the laminated structure of **primary troostite** which is formed when steel is rapidly cooled in its initial stage from a temperature below that which will produce martensite].

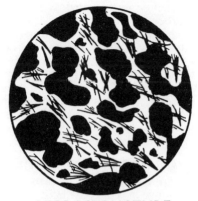

MICROSTRUCTURE

FIG. 6.7.
TROOSTITE. DARK CONSTITUENT OF TROOSTITE IN
AN ACICULAR STRUCTURE OF MARTENSITE. THIS
STRUCTURE IS OBTAINED WHEN STEEL IS COOLED
AT A RATE SLIGHTLY LESS RAPID THAN THAT
REQUIRED TO PRODUCE MARTENSITE; OR BY RE-
HEATING STEEL IN WHICH MARTENSITE HAS
ALREADY BEEN PRODUCED

Upon further reheating more carbon will separate out from the iron and the next transitional product will be **sorbite:** Fig. 6.8. This is a structure consisting of very fine particles of cementite in ferrite

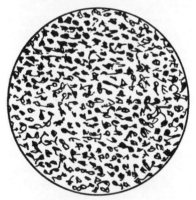

MICROSTRUCTURE

FIG. 6.8.
SORBITE.   A MIXTURE OF SMALL UNORIENTATED
PARTICLES OF CEMENTITE AND FERRITE. THIS STRUC-
TURE IS OBTAINED WHEN STEEL IS COOLED AT A
RATE SLIGHTLY LESS RAPID THAN THAT REQUIRED
TO PRODUCE TROOSTITE; OR AS A RESULT OF
TEMPERING STEEL AFTER QUENCHING AND
HARDENING

similar to pearlite but in the granular form rather than laminated. [This sorbitic structure is predominant in normalized steels].

Sorbite is not so hard as troostite but is much tougher with good all-round strength.

If this sorbitic structure is subjected to a continuation of heat all the remaining carbon will come out of solution with iron and alternate layers of cementite and ferrite will form to produce pearlite.

The transformation of austenite into pearlite depends therefore upon the amount of heat applied to the quenched steel and the formation by different cooling rates of the intermittent structures troostite and sorbite.

[The process of quenching heated steel whilst in the austenitic condition, followed by the formation and arrest of secondary structures by reheating, and further quenching is known as **hardening and tempering.** See Appendix 2, page 90].

THE CRITICAL RANGE IN PLAIN CARBON STEELS

The structural change that occurs in carbon steels on cooling from the austenitic range has already been discussed. However, this change (with the exception of full pearlitic steel) will take place over a range of temperatures known as the **critical range in steels.**

To understand this more fully a study should be made of part of the iron/carbon equilibrium diagram Fig. 6.9, as this will indicate the temperature at which the critical range will begin and end for all percentage carbon steels.

When any carbon steel cools from its austenitic condition a temperature will be reached when the face-centred cubic iron will transform to its body-centred cubic structure. This critical temperature is known as the **upper critical point** for all carbon steels and is line *CED* in Fig. 6.9.

If the steel at the upper critical point is of the hypoeutectoid type the transformation through the critical range will be from austenite to ferrite and pearlite. A hypereutectoid steel will revert from austenite to pearlite and cementite. It should be noted, however, that although the upper critical temperature varies considerably throughout the complete range of carbon steels the lower critical temperature at which the above transformations end is always constant. This is known as the **lower critical point** for all carbon steels, and is line *AEB* in Fig. 6.9.

When a full pearlitic steel of 0·83 per cent carbon content cools down from the austenitic range the transformation from austenite to pearlite will begin and end at the same temperature, and it is at this point, *E* in Fig. 6.9, that the upper critical and lower critical lines converge. This is called the **eutectoid point** and steels corresponding to this point are termed **eutectoid steels.**

Steels undergoing heat treatment in the form of full annealing or normalizing are always heated to just above their upper critical point Ac3. This is also the case when steels are to be heated and quenched to produce hardness prior to tempering. See Fig. 6.9.

[The upper critical point is referred to as the Ac3 point on heating and the Ar3 point on cooling.

The lower critical point is referred to as the Ac1 point on heating and the Ar1 point on cooling.

The Ac3 and Ac1 points are at a slightly higher temperature than the Ar3 and Ar1 points].

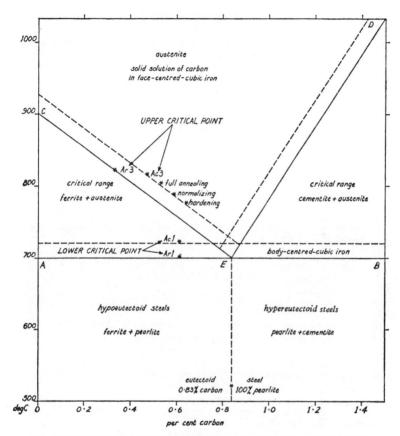

FIG. 6.9 PART OF THE IRON/CARBON EQUILIBRIUM DIAGRAM SHOWING HEAT
TREATMENT RANGES FOR PLAIN CARBON STEELS

QUESTIONS ON CHAPTER 6

(1) When a steel suffers HOT SHORTNESS it is mostly due to the presence of:
   (a) Sulphur
   (b) Phosphorus
   (c) Silicon
   (d) Manganese.

(2) Carbon occurs in steel in the combined state with iron to form the constituent:
   (a) Ferrite
   (b) Cementite
   (c) Pearlite
   (d) Bainite.

(3) When a steel is heated to above its upper critical temperature the structure produced is one of:
   (a) Martensite
   (b) Austenite
   (c) Pearlite
   (d) Sorbite.

(4) The predominant structure of a hypereutectoid steel that has been quenched at above its upper critical point will be:
   (a) Austenite
   (b) Martensite
   (c) Troostite
   (d) Sorbite.

(5) When a steel is subjected to a form of heat treatment known as TEMPERING after it has been hardened, the process is one of:
   (a) Heating without quenching
   (b) Heating and quenching
   (c) Heating and cooling slowly
   (d) Heating and hammering.

(Answers on page 100)

CHAPTER 7

Microscopic and Macroscopic Examination
The Analysis of Weld Metal Deposits by Macroscopic
Examination
The Analysis of the Heat-Affected Zone of the Parent
Metal by Macroscopic Examination `
Granular Formation Common to Heat-Affected Zone of
Weldments in the As-Welded Condition
Preheating

MICROSCOPIC AND MACROSCOPIC EXAMINATION

When a study is to be made of the chemical constituent of a
metal embracing crystal build-up and distribution as in a metallic
alloy the specimen will be subjected to a **microscopic examination.**
This consists of the viewing of very small areas of structure (micro-
structures) under high-power magnification after the metal's surface
has been polished and etched with the appropriate reagent.

Although microscopic examination is of great value to the
metallurgist the viewing of larger areas of surface, such as the cross-
section of a welded joint, under low-power magnification is of
greater value to the welding engineer. This is known as **macroscopic
examination.** The specimen is also polished and etched before
examination.

[A table of etching reagents for macroscopic examination is in
Appendix 3, page 91].

Macroscopic examination will reveal such defects as inter-
granular cracking, porosity, and non-metallic inclusions in the weld,
and will determine the granular structure in the weld metal and
heat-affected zone of the parent metal, especially when grain growth
has been severe.

This type of examination indicates the amount of dilution that
has taken place between weld metal and parent metal and therefore
signifies the depth of fusion that has taken place.

Various macrostructures of weld and parent metal will be
discussed later in this chapter.

THE ANALYSIS OF WELD METAL DEPOSITS
BY MACROSCOPIC EXAMINATION

The final structure produced in welds of various ferrous and
non-ferrous metals, particularly in their alloyed form, is often very
complicated; but the initial crystal growth taking place upon solidification will normally follow the same pattern in all weld metal
deposits and this crystal formation is often retained throughout the
whole cooling cycle.

From the point of view of its structure weld metal can be said to
be in the cast state.

The plate edges of the weld joint are usually much cooler than the liquid weld metal itself and therefore nuclei will form at these colder surfaces first.

The direction of crystal development will now be in the opposite direction to which the extraction of heat is taking place and, therefore, the crystals will grow predominantly inwards towards the centre of the cast mass.

The crystals so formed are extremely elongated, their lateral growth having been greatly reduced owing to early contact with adjacent crystals growing in the same direction. They are known as **columnar crystals,** and Fig. 7.1 shows this type of crystal formation

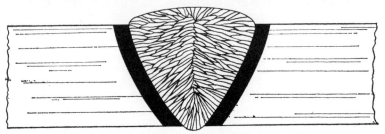

FIG. 7.1. THE MACROSTRUCTURE OF A SINGLE-RUN WELD DEPOSIT IN THE AS-WELDED CONDITION SHOWING COLUMNAR CRYSTAL FORMATION

which is generally found upon macroscopic examination of single-run weld deposits in their as-welded condition.

The mechanical properties produced by this type of coarse-grained structure are not very high and, therefore, heat treatment in the form of post-heating should be carried out upon the weld zone in order to bring about crystal refinement, especially if the welded joint is to undergo severe working conditions.

In multi-run welds, however, each run of weld deposited will re-heat the preceding run to such an extent that a considerable granular refinement will take place throughout the weld metal, although the last run of weld to be laid down will always remain in the coarse columnar condition as typified in Fig. 7.2. This fine-grained structure characteristic of multi-run deposits is often referred to as being **weld normalized,** the mechanical properties of this type of welded joint being superior to single-run weld beads.

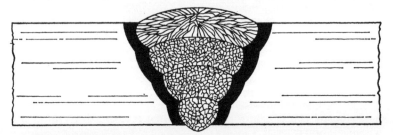

FIG. 7.2. THE MACROSTRUCTURE OF A MULTI-RUN WELD DEPOSIT IN THE AS-WELDED CONDITION SHOWING GRANULAR REFINEMENT IN CONSECUTIVE RUNS AND COLUMNAR CRYSTAL FORMATION IN THE CAPPING RUN

THE ANALYSIS OF THE HEAT-AFFECTED ZONE OF THE PARENT METAL BY MACROSCOPIC EXAMINATION

The amount of heat developed during welding is sufficient to have a marked effect upon the physical and mechanical properties of the parent metal within the welding zone itself, and the area of this heat-affected zone can vary considerably depending upon the thermal conduction of the metal and the form of welding process being adopted. Other factors that may influence the heat-affected zone can be the chemical constituent of the parent metal, its structural formation, mass and specific heat. Also, the conditions under which the welding operation is being carried out have to be taken into consideration, e.g. severe weather and general climatic conditions. See Appendix 8, page 96.

The desirable properties that can be produced in non-ferrous alloys by heat treatment and age-hardening are somewhat reduced in the heat-affected parent metal after welding, and further post-heat treatment will be required if these properties are to be regained. For instance, the softening effect on age-hardened aluminium-copper and magnesium-silicon alloys would tend to lower the tensile strength although this is not so pronounced as the reduction in tensile strength in the heat-affected zone of work-hardened materials. In carbon and alloy steels, however, the problems that arise in connection with the heat-affected zone are more numerous and important, especially when assessing the reliability of welded structure and components in service.

There is virtually no structural transformation in the heat-affected zone of low carbon steel after welding unless carbon **pick-up** has taken place during welding. But, when welding steels of higher carbon content, precautions must be taken to prevent undesirable structures forming in the heat-affected zone. The cooling of the weld area under normal conditions may be fast enough to produce martensite, and this extremely hard unbalanced structure can cause **hard zone cracking.** (See page 65).

Preheating is therefore necessary before welding these types of steel so that the cooling rate will be retarded and a more moderate structure produced.

Certain alloy steels, such as the air-hardening types, cannot be prevented from hardening even with very high preheating temperatures, although post-heating can be applied to modify the martensitic structure that has formed in the heat-affected zone. These steels, however, are susceptible to **underbead cracking** and they create special problems which are dealt with in the following chapter.

Steels of the austenitic and ferritic-austenitic types should preferably be maintained at the lowest possible temperature during welding so that the properties within the heat-affected zone will not be greatly disturbed.

GRANULAR FORMATION COMMON TO THE HEAT-AFFECTED ZONE OF WELDMENTS IN THE AS-WELDED CONDITION

The thermal cycle set up by welding can cause a wide range of temperature gradients in the parent metal (Fig. 3.1, page 19), consequently different grain structures are possible in the heat-affected zone. This zone itself extends from the fusion line which is the junction between weld dilution* and the unmelted base metal to the base metal which has not been sufficiently heated to alter the original structure.

The heat-affected zone can be divided into three sub-zones as shown in the schematic macro-structure of a welded joint, Fig. 7.3. The first sub-zone next to the weld deposit is the **overheated zone** which reaches a temperature very close to the melting point of the metal. Overheating causes severe grain growth, which is very pronounced throughout this first zone. The mechanical properties attributed to the parent metal will be somewhat reduced by this coarse structure unless post-weld heat treatment is carried out to bring about granular refinement.

The effects of grain growth have already been discussed under the section THE PROCESS OF COLD WORKING AND ANNEALING, page 41.

During the welding of carbon steel the temperature of the overheated zone will be well above the upper critical point, producing not only grain growth but also a coarse undesirable structure known as a **Widmanstätten structure.**

The second sub-zone can be called the **refining zone** for it is here that most parent metals reach a temperature sufficient to produce a complete recrystallization of the granular structure. In carbon steel, for instance, the section of metal in this second sub-zone will reach a transformation temperature just above the upper critical point long enough for austenite to form, followed by a cooling rate fast enough to prevent grain growth from taking place. This results in a fine-grained structure similar to that found in normalized steel.

The third and last sub-zone will reach a temperature only high enough for partial recrystallization to take place, and in the case of carbon steel it is often referred to as the **transition zone.** The parent steel will be heated to a temperature somewhere between the Ac1 and Ac3, therefore the transformation to austenite will not be complete. This can produce a complex structure which will remain after cooling. Beyond this third sub-zone lies the unaffected parent metal.

Figs. 7.4 and 7.5 show the type of structure normally seen in a macroscopic examination of the weld area when two metals in their annealed condition are joined together. Fig. 7.6 (p. 63) shows the type of structure normally observed in a macroscopic examination of the weld area when a metal in the annealed condition is joined to another metal in the cold worked condition.

*Some of the weld deposit will always combine with the parent metal to form an alloy. The properties of this alloy will largely determine the properties of the joint.

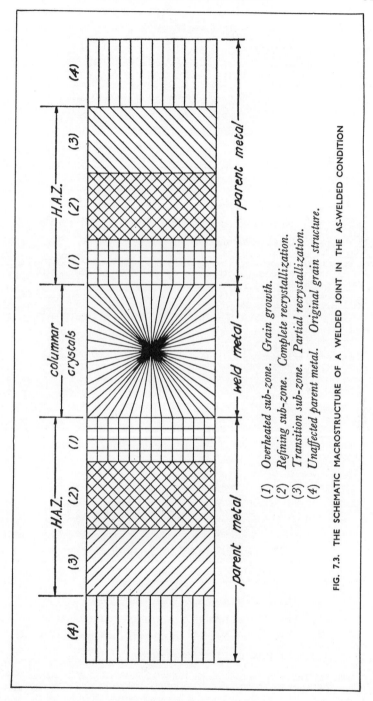

(1) Overheated sub-zone. Grain growth.
(2) Refining sub-zone. Complete recrystallization.
(3) Transition sub-zone. Partial recrystallization.
(4) Unaffected parent metal. Original grain structure.

FIG. 7.3. THE SCHEMATIC MACROSTRUCTURE OF A WELDED JOINT IN THE AS-WELDED CONDITION

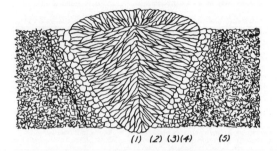

(1) *Weld metal, columnar crystal formation.*
(2) *Parent metal, overheated zone, grain growth.*
(3) *Parent metal, refining zone, complete recrystallization.*
(4) *Parent metal, transition zone, partial recrystallization.*
(5) *Parent metal, unaffected structure.*

FIG. 7.4. THE MACROSTRUCTURE OF THE WELD AREA WHEN TWO METALS IN
THEIR ANNEALED CONDITION ARE JOINED TOGETHER (BUTT WELD)

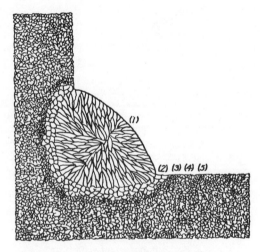

(1) *Weld metal, columnar crystal formation.*
(2) *Parent metal, overheated zone, grain growth.*
(3) *Parent metal, refining zone, complete recrystallization.*
(4) *Parent metal, transition zone, partial recrystallization.*
(5) *Parent metal, unaffected structure.*

FIG. 7.5. THE MACROSTRUCTURE OF THE WELD AREA WHEN TWO METALS IN
THEIR ANNEALED CONDITION ARE JOINED TOGETHER (FILLET WELD)

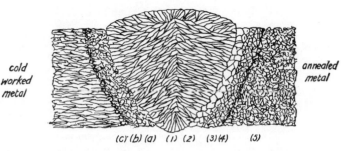

cold worked metal

annealed metal

(c)(b)(a) (1) (2) (3)(4) (5)

(1)   Weld metal, columnar crystal formation.

ANNEALED PARENT METAL

(2)   Overheated zone, grain growth.

(3)   Refining zone, complete recrystallization.

(4)   Transition zone, partial recrystallization.

(5)   Parent metal, unaffected annealed structure.

COLD-WORKED PARENT METAL

(a)   Refining zone, complete recrystallization.

(b)   Transition zone, partial recrystallization.

(c)   Parent metal, unaffected fibrous structure.

FIG. 7.6.   THE MACROSTRUCTURE OF THE WELD AREA WHEN A METAL IN THE ANNEALED CONDITION IS JOINED TO ANOTHER METAL IN THE COLD-WORKED CONDITION

PREHEATING

Although some use of preheating has already been discussed, further points on this pre-weld heat treatment are as follows:

(1) Preheating reduces the rate of cooling and therefore reduces the degree of hardness in the weld zone, which will raise ductility but lowers tensile strength.

(2) Preheating reduces weld shrinkage and therefore reduces the magnitude of shrinkage stresses although too high a preheating temperature will reduce the yield strength of the metal and may cause hot cracking in the weld zone.

(3) Preheating increases the depth of fusion and therefore increases weld dilution. This can be a disadvantage if undesirable elements from the parent metal are introduced into the weld metal; but it can be an advantage when welding alloy steels in the preheated condition. The pick up of elements may then be sufficient to compensate for loss of strength in the weld zone due to the slower cooling rate.

QUESTIONS ON CHAPTER 7

(1) The combination of acids recommended for the etching reagent when stainless steel is to undergo macroscopical examination is:

    (a) Hydrochloric plus Hydrofluoric
    (b) Hydrochloric plus Sulphuric
    (c) Hydrochloric plus Nitric
    (d) Hydrochloric plus Picric.

(2) The type of crystal normally found in a single-run arc weld in the as-welded condition is:

    (a) Equi-axed
    (b) Columnar
    (c) Polycrystalline
    (d) Dendritic.

(3) When weld metal refinement takes place in a multi-run deposit it is known by the term:

    (a) Weld annealing
    (b) Weld refining
    (c) Weld normalizing
    (d) Weld recrystallization.

(4) The first sub-zone in the HEAT-AFFECTED ZONE of the parent metal nearest the weld deposit will consist of:

    (a) Large crystal grains
    (b) Small crystal grains
    (c) Elongated crystal grains
    (d) Distorted crystal grains.

(5) Which one of the following statements is correct:

    (a) Preheating increases hardness
    (b) Preheating increases cooling
    (c) Preheating increases dilution
    (d) Preheating increases shrinkage stress?

(Answers on page 100)

CHAPTER 8

The Metallurgical Problems Associated with the Welding of
Plain Carbon Steels——Low-Alloy Steels
Stainless Steels——Cast Iron——and Hard Surfacing

THE WELDING OF PLAIN CARBON STEELS

Steels in the low-carbon group which include mild steel normally have a maximum carbon content of 0·25 per cent.

The lower tensile grades are mostly unkilled whilst the medium tensile grades can be in an unkilled or killed condition, silicon or manganese being used for the deoxidizing agent. The higher tensile grades are always semi-killed or completely killed, very often with the aid of aluminium as the reducing media. Steels in the first two grades are found in the "as-rolled" condition whereas the top grades are generally normalized after rolling.

The steels that have been killed with aluminium produce finer granular formations and achieve a satisfactory compromise between high strength and weldability, especially when combating brittle fracture in welded construction (see page 8).

Preheating of such steels is always recommended when large cross-sectional areas are to be joined together, for there is always a danger of hardening in the heat-affected zone even when the carbon content is as low as 0·15 per cent.

Steels in the medium carbon group (maximum 0·5% C) are generally more difficult to weld owing to their higher carbon content; for this reason preheating becomes more necessary as the percentage of carbon increases, especially if hardness figures are to be kept to a minimum. The metallurgical problems associated with this group are very similar to those involving low alloy steels and can be overcome much the same way. Reference Appendix 1.

THE WELDING OF LOW-ALLOY STEELS (HARD-ZONE CRACKING)

The common metallurgical problem associated with low-alloy steels is their susceptibility under welding conditions to produce bands of martensite, the Cr/Mo and Cr/Mo/V steels being very good examples.

The property of this martensitic structure will give rise to hardenability within the heat-affected zone of the parent metals and can also result in high hardness figures in the weld deposit itself.

Any hardness present in the weld area is always undesirable both from the point of serviceability and the danger of cracking taking place after welding, especially if the joint is welded under restraint. It is therefore essential that heat treatment in the form of pre-heating and in most cases post-heating to a prescribed temperature should be carried out when steels of this nature are to be fabricated by welding.

It has also been found that cracking can be overcome by using electrodes having a core structure of austenite or having a hydrogen controlled coating. This suggests that the presence of hydrogen can cause cracking within the hard martensitic structure. Parts of the heat-affected zone of the parent metals will have reached a temperature above the upper critical point and will therefore possess a complete structure of austenite. Hydrogen which has diffused from the weld deposit will be soluble in this austenitic formation although during the cooling cycle hydrogen will be precipitated as transformation from austenite to martensite takes place. As hydrogen is insoluble in martensite it will collect in micro-fissures throughout this harden structure until the build-up of pressure will be sufficient to cause a granular breakdown in the form of an inter-granular fracture. Thus it will be noted that by the use of austenitic weld metal, diffusion of hydrogen is reduced owing to its retention in the weld deposit, therefore a combination between austenitic electrodes and low hydrogen coatings would eliminate the undesirable effects brought about by **hard-zone cracking** (which is also referred to as **under-bead cracking**). See photograph B on page 101.

THE AIR-HARDENING GROUP OF ALLOY STEELS

Although the Nickel/Chrome steels that comprise this group of ferrous alloys have a weldability similar to that of the low-alloy steels, the metallurgical problem always associated with these air-hardening steels is that no post-weld treatment will retard the cooling rate sufficiently to prevent the formation of martensite. Consequently, extreme hardness will always be present in the heat-affected zone of the weld although post-annealing will help to alleviate to a great extent this undesirable property.

The pre-heating of air-hardening steels can afford protection from cracking during welding especially in multi-run welds, but the pre-heat temperature must always be kept fairly low. The influence of a high heat input upon such a material can only tend to increase the amount of martensitic transformation taking place after welding, thus creating a wider area of resultant hardness in the weldment.

THE WELDING OF STAINLESS STEEL

The corrosion resistance of stainless steel depends primarily upon the metallic element **chromium** which forms a continuous surface layer of chromic oxide when present in the steel in amounts exceeding 11 per cent. Chromium will also confer heat resistance to the steel. Other metallic elements are also added to enhance the mechanical properties of stainless steel as well as to increase its resistance against certain corrosive media. It is necessary therefore that weld deposits should always have adequate chromium content and such additional alloying elements as are present in the parent metals being joined so as to maintain a continuity of corrosion resistance throughout the weldment.

Although there are many different grades of stainless steel they can all be classified under three main headings:

    (a) Martensitic

    (b) Ferritic

    (c) Austenitic

MARTENSITIC STAINLESS STEEL

This type of stainless steel has a tendency to harden when cooled from high temperature. The welding of such a material will therefore create many problems due to the hardening effect that can be produced within the heat-affected areas of the parent metal and to some extent in the deposited weld metal. In order to reduce this hardness and subsequent brittleness special precautions can be taken in the form of pre-heating and post-heat treatment.

An important factor that must be taken into consideration before welding any particular stainless steel is its carbon level. The amount of carbon present in relationship to the amount of chromium in the steel will have a direct effect upon the subsequent hardness. With an increase of carbon the stainless steel will become progressively harder and therefore less suitable for welding owing to the possibility of cracking.

Martensitic stainless steels are susceptible to various forms of heat treatment resulting in a wide range of physical and mechanical properties. These are very important when a combination of corrosion, heat and creep resistance is called for in service.

FERRITIC STAINLESS STEEL

There is no appreciable hardening as a result of heat treatment to any stainless steels in this group owing to their very low carbon level, but there is a tendency towards brittleness if the steel has been exposed to elevated temperatures. This is said to be due to excessive grain growth which will be retained on cooling resulting in an as-welded deposit of low ductility. Pre-heating and post-heat treatment will help to modify this mechanical deficiency by improving ductility through recrystallization. Compensation for dilution should always be taken into consideration when selecting filler material for joining stainless steels in the ferritic group.

AUSTENITIC STAINLESS STEEL

The outstanding feature with this group of steels is the retention of **austenite** within the structure due to an addition of **nickel** to the chromium steels. This austenitic condition, which remains on cooling, renders these chrome/nickel steels non-hardening to any form of heat treatment and even fast cooling rates from high temperatures will actually soften them, although mostly all stainless steels in the austenitic condition will harden rapidly when subjected to cold working. They also have exceptional strength and excellent resistance to corrosion at elevated temperatures.

Austenitic stainless steels are much more amenable to welding than the Martensitic or the Ferritic types and for this reason most of the weldable stainless steels are from this range although welding problems such as severe **distortion, sigma phase** and **weld decay** can exist if precautions are not taken. Each of these problems will be dealt with separately.

DISTORTION IN AUSTENITIC STAINLESS STEEL

The amount of distortion that takes place as a direct result of welding can be excessive unless adequate precautions are taken (see Chapter 3). The magnitude of this distortion is due to the material having a very high coefficient of expansion, coupled with a very low heat conductivity.

SIGMA PHASE IN AUSTENITIC STAINLESS STEEL

The presence of **ferrite** in austenitic stainless steels containing a high proportion of ferrite-forming elements tends to produce brittleness when passing through the temperature range from 600°C to 900°C during the process of welding. This is due to the formation of a type of structure known as "Sigma phase."

Sigma is an extremely brittle constituent which can form in multi-run weld deposits when heavy sections are being joined together and will also occur to a more serious extent when heat treatment is carried out after welding.

It should be noted that although the presence of sufficient nickel will reduce the formation of ferrite, thus preventing the occurrence of a "Sigma phase", it will not combat the formation of ferrite if the stainless steel is subjected to prolonged heating during or after welding.

On the other hand the presence of ferrite does reduce hot cracking during welding, more so than when the steel is fully austenitic.

WELD DECAY IN AUSTENITIC STAINLESS STEEL

When steels of this type having a chromium content of 18 per cent and a nickel content of 8/10 per cent are heated through a temperature range from 500°C to 800°C they undergo a structural change which is detrimental to their corrosion resistant properties.

During welding part of the heat-affected zone of the parent metal will be maintained within the critical temperature for sufficient time to allow this physical defect to take place. Hence the term "weld decay".

The cause of this change is due to the precipitation of chromium carbides at the grain boundaries resulting in a chromium deficiency in the grains themselves.

This reduction in chromium is directly responsible for a severe decrease in the metal's ability to resist corrosion and therefore deterioration of the plate adjacent to the line of weld will take place under service conditions.

The addition of stabilizing elements having a stronger affinity for carbon than chromium are now added to this type of steel so that welding does not affect their resistance to corrosion.

Such carbide-forming elements are niobium and titanium and any carbide precipitation will therefore consist of niobium carbides or titanium carbides, consequently chromium deficiency within the granular structure does not occur.

Niobium is used in preference to titanium for the latter has an affinity for oxygen and will readily oxidize during welding operations.

There are other methods to prevent weld decay taking place such as a reduction in carbon content or by heat treatment in the form of high temperature heating followed by quenching.

The addition of ferrite-forming elements can also act as a prevention but the addition of carbide-forming elements as already mentioned is the most common method used in the manufacture of weldable austenitic stainless steel.

THE WELDING OF CAST IRON

Cast iron has a carbon content of between 2 and 4 per cent and is similar in structure to that of pig iron which is a product of the blast furnace already mentioned in Chapter 2.

The formation of carbon in cast iron can be as a carbide of iron (cementite) or as coarse graphite flakes; it is these two different forms of carbon that dictate the properties of the metal.

When cementite is predominant an extremely hard structure is formed producing a fracture surface having a whitish appearance. In this form the cast iron is known as **white cast iron.**

When the carbon is present as graphite the structure is much more stable and softer giving the fracture surface a greyish appearance. In this form the cast iron is known as **grey cast iron.**

The two types of cast iron are governed by the rate of cooling after casting or welding.

A high rate of cooling tends to prevent the decomposition of cementite; whereas if the cooling rate is controlled the carbon will have time to precipitate and free graphite will be produced.

The addition of silicon to iron castings will help to break down cementite but only under favourable conditions. If the cooling rate is too rapid the silicon will have no influence whatsoever; the cementite which is the predominant structure when the casting is at high temperature "especially welding temperature" will remain.

The precautions to be taken when welding cast iron are mostly dealt with in welding technology.

The only metallurgical problem is the structural changes already discussed that can take place if the cooling of the casting is not regulated after welding repairs have been carried out.

MALLEABLE CAST IRON

Malleable iron castings are initially produced as white cast iron before the process of malleablizing is employed. Two such methods can be used which will produce two types of casting: one being known as **Whiteheart** malleable iron; and the other **Blackheart** malleable iron.

These names refer to the respective structural fracture of the two irons after they have been annealed. Whiteheart has a whitish crystalline form and Blackheart a blackish crystalline form. The former is due to the presence of pearlite and the latter to the presence of graphite.

In the Whiteheart process the castings are combined with a mixture of used and new hematite ore and heated at an elevated temperature over a period of days before being finally cooled down very slowly. As a result of this process a portion of the carbon is oxidized, producing changes from ferrite to ferrite and pearlite throughout the casting with interspersed nodules of graphite.

In the Blackheart process the castings are combined with a mixture of sand and granulated slag and then heated to a prescribed temperature. As a result of this particular process very little oxidation of the carbon occurs and therefore the cementite breaks down into iron and small interspersed particles of carbon.

SPHEROIDAL GRAPHITE CAST IRON

In this type of cast iron the graphite is in the form of spheroids. This spheroidal graphite is formed by the presence of a small proportion of magnesium within the structure of the cast iron. The discontinuities that are created by the presence of graphite flakes in ordinary grey cast iron are eliminated; therefore spheroidal graphite will improve the mechanical properties of the resultant material.

This type of casting is fully responsive to all normal heat-treatments covering stress relieving, annealing, normalizing, hardening and tempering.

In the cast state this material has a structure of pearlite which will give a greater strength than flaked-graphite cast iron. When pearlitic spheroidal graphite castings are annealed the matrix structure becomes ferritic whereupon the combined carbon is broken down to be distributed as graphite spheroids within the ferritic matrix. In this condition the material exhibits its maximum toughness and ductility.

Unlike ordinary grey cast iron the spheroidal graphite cast irons show a stress/strain curve very similar to that of carbon steel, there being a direct relationship between stress and strain until a distinct yield point is reached.

THE DEPOSITION OF WEAR-RESISTING MATERIALS

Weld deposits used in hardsurfacing are generally classified under two groups of metallic alloys having austenitic or martensitic micro-structures, the selection of the deposit depending chiefly upon the service environment of the weldment.

The characteristic properties associated with the austenitic group are of moderately low hardness but possess a great capacity for work-hardening due to the breakdown of austenite. This structural change under working conditions produces a surface layer of martensite having a high resistance to abrasion whilst the underlying metal remains austenitic with properties that are softer but tougher.

A combination of hardness, toughness and resistance to impact is thus available with this group of metallic alloys without the need of thermal hardening treatment to which they are not susceptible.

As a contrast to the austenitic group the martensitic alloys have initial hardness which is not greatly affected by cold work.

The weld deposits are susceptible to varying degrees of hardness by heat treatment, consequently the hardness of a deposit will largely depend upon the rate of cooling after welding.

The unregulated cooling of the weld deposit under normal conditions will produce adequate hardness without subsequent heat treatment, although quenching from welding temperatures frequently produces extreme hardness if this is required in service. The amount of dilution that has taken place between the weld metal and base metal will also have to be taken into consideration as this has a direct affect upon the final hardness of the deposit.

It should be noted that high hardness is usually associated with greater resistance to wear but lower resistance to impact.

When excessive reclaiming has to be carried out it is always advisable to avoid heavy deposits of hardfacing materials, and for this reason a layer of weld metal having lower hardness values should first be deposited so that it will act as a buffer layer between the soft base and the final hardsurface. The main purpose of this intermediate buffer layer is to prevent spalling (cracking and flaking) that can occur owing to the inability of large hardsurfacing deposits to accommodate the considerable shrinkage stresses that are invariably set up upon cooling.

This layer will also prevent the hardsurface from being squeezed into the softer base metal under impact or load during severe service conditions.

See reference to work-hardening manganese steels, page 47.

QUESTIONS ON CHAPTER 8

(1) The purpose of PREHEATING low-alloy steel pipes before they are electric-arc welded is to:

    (a) Refine grain structure
    (b) Relieve internal stress
    (c) Retard rapid cooling
    (d) Regulate excessive expansion.

(2) Hard-zone cracking in low-alloy steel due to welding is the result of an absorbtion of:

    (a) Nitrogen
    (b) Oxygen
    (c) Hydrogen
    (d) Carbon.

(3) When a steel has more than 11 per cent of chromium added to it, the resultant alloy is known as:

    (a) High tensile steel
    (b) Low-alloy steel
    (c) Creep-resistant steel
    (d) Stainless steel.

(4) If an austenitic stainless steel weld was quenched whilst it was still at a high temperature, it would become:

    (a) Softer
    (b) Harder
    (c) Stronger
    (d) Weaker.

(5) Which one of the following properties is related to CAST IRON:

    (a) Ductility
    (b) Malleability
    (c) Plasticity
    (d) Brittleness?

(Answers on page 100)

CHAPTER 9

*The Metallurgical Problems Associated with the Welding of
Copper and its Alloys — Aluminium Alloys — Magnesium
Alloys — Nickel Alloys Including Clad Steels (Dilution) —
Titanium and its Alloys*

THE WELDING OF COPPER AND ITS ALLOYS
Copper

The versatility of copper in the field of mechanical, civil and domestic engineering makes it possibly the most important of the more common non-ferrous metals, especially when it is used to form the basis of a range of non-ferrous alloys under the headings of Brass and Bronze as well as alloys containing aluminium and nickel.

Copper can be classified under two main groups: **Oxygen-bearing copper,** and **Oxygen-free copper,** and although both groups possess the same basic characteristics (for instance, thermal expansion and thermal conduction) their mechanical properties can be greatly affected by the presence of oxides or the addition of small amounts of non-ferrous elements such as phosphorus and arsenic.

During the manufacture of copper a process of oxidation to extract impurities from the melt takes place which results in a metal being produced not entirely free of oxygen. This type of copper, named "Tough pitch", is not readily weldable by most fusion processes owing to the presence of copper oxide within the metal's microstructure which makes the copper susceptible to gas embrittlement if during the welding process a hydrogen atmosphere is present. A reduction in strength and ductility, as well as hot and cold shortness (cracking), can also be attributed to the concentration of oxides which are rejected on to the grain boundaries when this type of copper is subjected to high temperature, although these oxides do not greatly reduce the corrosion resistant properties of the metal itself.

The refinement of oxygen-bearing copper can, however, take place upon the removal of the oxygen by reduction methods. Phosphorus, zinc or hydrogen is used as the reducing agent. This deoxidized copper can be welded by most fusion processes, although the specific heat of the metal brings into existence problems of high heat input which can contribute to a reduction in strength as a result of overheating, and severe distortion taking place if adequate precautions are not taken before and during welding.

Brass

The brasses comprise a wide range of alloys consisting primary of **copper** and **zinc,** although small quantities of such elements as iron, manganese, aluminium, tin, nickel and silicon are sometimes added to produce special high tensile materials.

The properties of the straight brasses, however, depend largely on the ratio of zinc to copper present in the alloy and an increase of zinc at the expense of copper will have a great influence on the structural changes that will inevitably take place.

When, for instance, the alloy consists of 70 per cent copper and 30 per cent zinc (cartridge brass) the crystal structure produced will be one of a uniform solid solution consisting of zinc dissolved in copper. This type of structure is known as an **alpha** solid solution and brasses within this range are named **alpha brasses.** Under favourable conditions of controlled annealing and cooling the alpha brasses can contain up to 38 per cent zinc before other constituents begin to form. Alpha brasses are generally manufactured in the form of sheet wire and tube having good strength combined with good ductility when in the cold state thus rendering these alloys in the category of cold work materials possessing the ability to work-harden and to be subsequently softened by annealing (recrystallization).

Upon a further increase of zinc to produce such alloys as **Muntz metal** (60 per cent copper and 40 per cent zinc) a second solid solution rich in zinc is formed. This new crystal structure is known as a **beta** solid solution and, along with the **alpha** solid solution, produces a duplex structure to form a range of alloys known as the **alpha/beta brasses** which have a maximum of 45 per cent zinc. Owing to an increase in hardness brought about by this second constituent the alpha/beta alloys have properties somewhat different from the alpha alloys and, although this increased hardness produces greater tensile strength to the material, the reduction in ductility can be so marked as to render these brasses incapable of being worked to any great extent in their cold state without fracture. The working properties of the alpha/beta alloys are, however, enhanced by an application of heat and can therefore be formed by many hot working processes. These alloys are also manufactured in their cast state to produce the bulk of all general purpose brass castings.

The main problem associated with the welding of brass is the volatilization of zinc from the alloy. This loss of zinc due to its low boiling point can reduce the properties of the weldment most severely and for this reason the burning out of zinc must be kept to a minimal amount. In the gas welding process a retention of zinc during the welding of brass is achieved by an excess of oxygen in the welding flame which produces an oxidizing condition on the surface of the molten metal thus preventing volatilization from taking place. This problem can become more serious when alloys containing zinc are joined by the metal arc welding process and to combat the volatile tendency of zinc during welding the shortest possible arc must always be maintained using electrodes having a core wire of phosphor-bronze. A certain degree of pre-heat is always beneficial when welding the brasses and the pre-heat temperature will generally increase with increase of zinc content, the range of temperature being between a minimum of 250°C and a maximum of 400°C. Low temperature annealing is also recommended for cold worked brass weldments that are to be subjected to a corrosive environment during service. This is to prevent **season cracking** taking place, which is a defect brought about by internal stresses being set up by cold forming of the material and by thermal contraction due to welding, combined with exposure to certain corrosive media.

Bronze

The true bronzes are essentially alloys of copper and tin and are referred to as **tin bronzes.** They fall into two categories depending on the amount of tin present in the alloy: the wrought materials having a range from 1 per cent to 9 per cent tin and the cast materials having a range from 9 per cent to 25 per cent tin.

These bronzes are also known as **phosphor-bronzes** owing to the presence of a residual amount of phosphorus which has been used as a deoxidizing agent during smelting; or the addition of phosphorus to improve the tenacity of the material.

Although tin bronzes are of great importance to industrial engineering, additional elements such as lead and zinc are frequently present to produce special metallurgical conditions. The alloying of lead, for instance, will produce a bronze having excellent machining and bearing properties but the additional element impedes welding. The addition of zinc will produce alloys known as **gun metals** which are mostly in the form of castings having a high degree of strength coupled with good corrosion resistance. These are readily weldable.

The welding of the wrought tin bronze alloys does not present great difficulties although care should always be taken to ensure that the minimum of restraint is put upon the weld joints themselves. This precaution is due to the fact that these alloys have a wide freezing range and, therefore, hot shortness can take place if stresses are set up when shrinkage of the weld metal takes place during solidification. In the molten condition these bronzes can also absorb a large quantity of gases which are then liberated during this solidification range. Pre-heating can improve welding conditions, but is only normally carried out on heavy section and never exceeds 200°C.

When the tin bronzes are in their cast condition a coarse dendritic structure prevails which will result in a weld deposit having inferior mechanical properties. This undesirable condition can, however, be modified by the use of straight or stringer weld bead deposits which are then peened (light hammered) whilst still at a high temperature, thus tending to refine the structure of the casting.

Post-heat treatment up to a temperature of 500°C, followed by fast cooling, can be carried out if maximum ductility is required, but it is not an essential operation after welding.

COPPER-ALUMINIUM ALLOYS (ALUMINIUM BRONZE)

These alloys, which contain between 5 and 15 per cent aluminium, are readily weldable without preheating if the aluminium content is kept fairly high. However, as the percentage of aluminium is reduced the resultant alloy will have a tendency to hot short and cracking may occur during welding.

THE WELDING OF ALUMINIUM ALLOYS

Aluminium in its pure state lacks good mechanical properties thus making it unsuitable for most engineering purposes.

The addition of other elements, however, can produce such a marked improvement in these properties as to raise the tensile strength of some aluminium alloys to that of many ferrous alloys. Some of these alloying elements also have a direct influence on the material's susceptibility to heat treatment other than annealing, whereas other additions have no influence whatsoever.

The aluminium alloys can therefore be classified under two main headings: **heat-treatable alloys,** and **non-heat treatable alloys,** both of which can be produced in the wrought or cast form.

The non-heat treatable alloys depend largely on elements such as iron, manganese and silicon to increase their strength and resistance to corrosion, as well as to promote work-hardening properties. The loss of ductility that will normally take place when these alloys are cold worked can be regained by post-annealing. The resultant effects produced when welding these materials in their worked-hardened condition will be similar to the process of annealing, thus bringing about an improvement in ductility at the expense of initial strength in the heat-affected zone of the parent metal, whilst the weld metal itself will remain in the as-cast condition. The heat-treatable alloys are of a more complex nature and rely mostly on precipitation hardening to produce their maximum strength. This hardening effect can be brought about by the use of such alloying elements as magnesium and copper.

Copper, for example, will become much more soluble in aluminium as a rise in temperature is recorded resulting in an increase in the amount of solid solution formed in the Al/Cu alloy. This solid solubility can be retained if the alloy is subjected to a process of rapid cooling leaving the copper in an unstabled condition of super saturation. Over a period of time, however, soluble stability will be achieved by the steady precipitation of **excess** copper in micro-form on to the grain-boundaries causing an internal strain to be set up in the structure with sufficient magnitude to impart additional hardness and strength to the aluminium alloy without greatly impairing ductility. This metallurgical condition is often referred to as **age hardening.**

Although control of strength, hardness and ductility can be achieved by solution heat treatment, a variation in these properties can also be greatly influenced by the elements used in alloying and by the amount part precipitation of the micro-constituent has taken place. A modification to the properties of heat-treatable alloys will also occur as a result of welding heat. This is due to an un-controlled form of solution and precipitation taking place in the heat-affected zone of the material with the forming of sub-zones where heat input has been sufficient to dissolve soluble constituents which are partially retained in solid solution; and where overaging will be predominant due to prolonged precipitation together with a coalescence of particles of such soluble constituents.

A strength comparable to the original can be achieved in the heat affected zone by a suitable heat treatment after welding.

Most welding difficulties are derived from the physical nature of aluminium which will include a high expansion and conduction rate coupled with a high heat capacity (specific heat). Also, the fact that an adherent refractory oxide film is always present on the surface of the metal with a melting point in the region of 2050°C compared to 660°C for that of aluminium.

Other problems to be taken into consideration are the metal's susceptibility to hot shortness which is mainly a function of composition and can therefore be remedied to some extent by depositing weld metal as far removed as possible from the peak cracking composition. The high rate of hydrogen absorption that can take place when aluminium is at welding temperature results in structural porosity. The corrosion resistance of some aluminium alloys can also be affected by welding if there is a change in con-stituent segregation, or that other elements such as iron and silicon have been introduced into the alloy-forming constituents which will greatly reduce the material's resistance to certain corrosive media.

THE WELDING OF MAGNESIUM ALLOYS

The main welding problems are mostly confined to the magnesium-aluminium and magnesium-zinc alloys. Aluminium, for instance, can increase the stress-corrosion sensitivity of a weldment although this undesirable condition can be much reduced by stress-relieving. Whereas the tendency towards cracking in the weld area is always predominant whenever zinc is present.

In contrast, the magnesium alloys which contain zirconium and thorium do not create welding problems. Thorium will even enhance weldability by helping to reduce weld cracking.

The non-heat treatable magnesium alloys, although dependent on work-hardening for their optimum strength, should always be welded when in the annealed condition as this helps to keep grain growth in the heat-affected zone down to a minimum.

The metallurgical problems associated with the welding of the heat-treatable age hardening alloys are very similar to those asso-ciated with the aluminium alloys in the same category (see previous section). The as-welded deposit in most magnesium alloys retains a fine grain structure thus giving a high degree of strength. When failure does occur it will be mostly confined to the heat-affected zones where mechanical properties are somewhat reduced.

Other weldability problems are comparable to those of aluminium alloys in regard to high melting point of surface oxide, high thermal conduction and expansion rates (see previous section).

THE WELDING OF NICKEL AND NICKEL ALLOYS

Nickel and its alloys are greatly susceptible to sulphur and lead contamination, especially at welding temperature; this enrichment of sulphur or lead can lead to severe hot cracking. Other forms of cracking can also occur due to the presence of an excess of silicon, or if the materials are welded whilst they are still in a work-hardened condition. The low ductility associated with nickel-rich alloys when at elevated temperatures can also produce cracking, particularly if welding is carried out under any form of restrain. Defects such as cracking, already mentioned, or weld porosity resulting from high iron inducement and gas absorption during welding can be controlled by changing the composition of the filler material from that of the parent material although both weld and parent metals should always match up as close as possible to produce maximum strength. Great care should be taken when welding the heat-treatable nickel alloys that develop their optimum properties by the introduction of age-hardening which is produced after solution treatment. This process is similar to that used in the age-hardening of heat-treatable aluminium alloys: see page 76.

In general, these nickel alloys are supplied in their solution-treated condition and undergo age-hardening after welding; but due to the process of welding a narrow band is formed adjacent to the weld deposit which does not have the properties of the parent material. However, these inferior properties can be restored to their original state if a full heat-treatment including solution-treatment and ageing takes place after welding. Since the welding of these heat-treatable alloys involve a serious risk of stress-cracking, attention should always be given to the amount of thermal stress set up in the weldment. This can be greatly reduced by using a pattern of welding sequences. Although the filler material used in the welding of heat-treatable alloys may vary slightly from that of the parent metal it can still be of an age-hardening type and will therefore respond to the same treatment as that carried out on the parent metal although not so susceptible to stress-cracking as the fully heat-treated base metal.

In conclusion, the weldability of the age-hardening nickel alloys is closely associated with material conditions prior to welding inasmuch as the parent metals should always be in the annealed condition before fabrication and welding. Inter-annealing may be required during these operations to reduce any residual stress that may have been set up which would increase the tendency to cracking when the material's ageing temperature was reached.

THE WELDING OF CLAD STEELS

When a steel is rendered corrosion-resistant by having a bonded layer of nickel or a nickel alloy covering one of its surfaces it is generally referred to as a **clad steel.**

The important factors to be observed when welding this class of steel include the continuity of the cladding and a high joint strength throughout the entire fabrication.

As two greatly contrasting metals are involved the main metallurgical problem associated with welding is mostly one of dilution. This can result from interfusion taking place if two different filler materials are used, and although this can be remedied if the joint is completed with only weld metal having the composition of the cladding, dilution can still take place between one filler material and the steel portion of the parent plate.

The general procedure in the joining of clad steel comprises making two separate welds.

When certain cladding alloys are welded first, the steel deposit when laid down can interfuse with these cladding materials to produce martensitic structures within the steel portion of the joint, Careful heat control and welding technique can minimize this hardening effect from taking place, but the danger of cracking, or a reduction in ductility sufficient to render undesirable mechanical properties to the joint, are always present.

If the steel section is welded before the cladding layer the forming of such hard brittle constituents can be avoided; but contamination of the cladding alloy will now take place due to a migration of iron. This interfusion of iron is normally restricted to the first weld deposit and therefore it is always beneficial to have a layer of cladding of sufficient thickness to accommodate a weld consisting of at least two passes.

The reduction in corrosion resistance due to dilution can often be offset by the use of filler material having an alloy content in excess of that required to produce the same results under service environment, if such an iron pickup had not taken place.

DILUTION

The process of welding facilitates the melting of the base metals along the joint faces and the deposition of filler material also in the molten condition. When a combination of these two metals takes place an alloy is formed with properties that will largely determine the properties of the welded joint although when filler metal and base metal are of the same composition the admixture will have little effect upon these properties. Metals of different constituents often produce resultant alloys lacking the requirements needed to obtain a satisfactory welded joint especially if the base metals to be joined are themselves of different alloying materials to each other.

In a joint between dissimilar metals the physical as well as the mechanical properties must be taken into consideration when establishing the type of filler material to be used, owing to the differences that can occur to these properties due to the resultant microstructure. The filler material must also have properties compatible with both base metal and with service environment. When a migration of elements takes place that will result in the enrichment of one metal or alloy at the expense of another metal or alloy it is referred to as **dilution.** The degree of dilution will be governed by the amount of heat input during a particular welding procedure. See photographs on page 107.

TITANIUM AND ITS ALLOYS

Elements such as aluminium, copper, manganese, molybdenum, tin, vanadium and zirconium are alloyed with titanium to enhance strength and other mechanical properties. Although such properties are greatly affected by small amounts of oxygen and nitrogen in solid solution, the strength and hardness will increase as greater quantities of these gases are present, with a reduction in ductility as the purity of the metal is reduced. The strength of titanium decreases with a rise in temperature owing to progressive deterioration by oxidation, although this can be greatly overcome by the use of titanium alloys. Titanium can withstand attack by various aggressive media and in many cases its corrosion resistance is superior to that of stainless steel. Wrought titanium can be worked in the hot or cold condition and will undergo the process of annealing. Various heat treatments can be carried out on certain titanium alloys and in the solution-treated condition the titanium/molybdenum alloys have high ductility and when fully aged will produce a high degree of strength.

THE WELDING OF TITANIUM AND ITS ALLOYS

The gas shielded tungsten arc is generally recommended for the welding of titanium and its alloys owing to the many advantages this process has to offer. The shielding gases used in this process are very important in the production of high strength homogeneous welds. Owing to the high affinity that titanium has for oxygen, sound welded joints are extremely difficult to produce. For this reason the welding area is usually further protected by auxiliary shielding having an inert gas atmosphere. The purity of the shielding gases has a marked influence on the mechanical properties of the weld, and as moisture is so detrimental to these properties a measurement of the dew point of the gas or the gas mixture being used is a precautionary measure that should be undertaken. Moisture pickup can greatly affect hardness and ductility and can also induce stress-corrosion cracking. Stress relief is recommended in complex weldments because residual stresses will cause low endurance limits in high cycle fatigue. In the joining of titanium a filler material having a slightly lower strength than the parent metal is recommended. The migration of constituents during welding will tend to strengthen the weld. As the filler metal is relatively pure it will tolerate a high diffusion rate from the parent metal before toughness and ductility are seriously impaired. The joining of titanium with such metals as steel, copper, aluminium and nickel, where intermetallic compounds are formed, produce brittle joints. Intermetallic compounds are not formed when niobium, molybdenum, vanadium and ziconium are joined to titanium therefore welds are produced which have varying levels of mechanical properties.

QUESTIONS ON CHAPTER 9

(1) Which one of the following gases renders copper unfit for fusion welding:

    (a) Hydrogen
    (b) Oxygen
    (c) Nitrogen
    (d) Argon?

(2) Which one of the following alloys can suffer from HOT SHORTNESS owing to the wide freezing range it passes through after welding:

    (a) Wrought brass
    (b) Wrought tin/bronze
    (c) Cast gun metal
    (d) Cast Muntz metal?

(3) Which one of the following metals will cause AGE PRECIPITATION hardening to take place in heat-treatable aluminium:

    (a) Copper
    (b) Zinc
    (c) Tin
    (d) Lead?

(4) Nickel is greatly susceptible to sulphur contamination during welding and this enrichment of sulphur can produce:

    (a) Cold cracking
    (b) Hot cracking
    (c) Hard-zone cracking
    (d) Season cracking.

(5) The main metallurgical problem associated with the welding of clad steels is one of:

    (a) Dilution
    (b) Precipitation
    (c) Oxidation
    (d) Distortion.

(Answers on page 100)

CHAPTER 10

NON-DESTRUCTIVE METHODS OF TESTING

MAGNETIC CRACK TEST

There are two methods of magnetic crack testing.

METHOD 1. Iron filings in a finely divided state are suspended in paraffin—this mixture being termed **magnetic fluid.**

The specimen under test is magnetized and the fluid is then painted on the metal which must have a machined or polished surface.

If there are any cracks in the metal an alteration in the magnetic field occurs at the crack and as a result the finely divided particles of iron cling to the edges of the crack and show it up as a dark hair-line.

The disadvantages with this method is that it can only be applied to most ferrous materials. It will only show up surface cracks and the specimen must be machined or polished to produce good results.

METHOD 2. In this method the specimen is magnetized as before or by having a heavy current passed through it, and search coils connected to a galvanometer are moved over the specimen. If a crack exists in the metal the change of magnetic field across it will cause a change of current in the search coil and this is indicated by fluctuations of the galvanometer needle.

TESTING WITH DYE PENETRANTS

In this method the penetrant is of a suitable dye solution, usually red in colour, which is drawn by capillary action into any surface discontinuities. A developer with a chalky base is then applied to the surface. This chemical dries on contact and is stained by the dye which rises to the surface again by capillary action. Cracks and pores are then revealed as red dots, or continuous red lines, respectively. The spread of the dye indicates fairly accurately the measure of the flaw. An essential requirement in this method is the pre-cleaning of the weldment as this is essential to obtain a high degree of sensitivity. The penetrant is applied either by spraying or immersion, the "contact" time varying from a few minutes to about an hour. The excess penetrant is then removed, usually by running water. The developer is then lightly applied by spraying and within a few minutes the surface is ready for inspection.

TESTING WITH FLUORESCENT PENETRANTS

This method requires the weld to be examined by an ultra-violet light source and the penetrants that are used act either by a direct fluorescent from within the flaw or crack when dry, or are drawn out through the agency of a developer.

The penetrant used is generally a fluorescent ink applied to the cleaned surface either by spraying or immersion. Under examination with a suitable ultra-violet lamp, the defect is soon visible as an intense green colouration.

ULTRASONIC TESTING

The ultrasonic flaw detector will generate small pulses of energy and when applied to electric crystals usually made from quartz, barium titanate or lead zirconate, they are converted to mechanical vibrations in a probe. These vibrations are injected into the material under examination and will travel forward in a near parallel beam through this material until they reach a discontinuity where they will be reflected at an angle equal to the angle of incidence, and returned to the probe. Because the waves in various materials are known, it is possible to measure fairly accurately the path travelled by the beam and the position of defects present if the initial pulse is applied to the timebase of an oscilloscope and the reflected pulse applied at a later fraction of time by calibrating the source of the reflection.

There are various techniques used in the examination of welds. The single probe method where the ultrasonic waves are reflected from any defects present and returned to the probe (Fig. 10.1); or the double-probe method where separate transmitting and receiving probes are used, one either side of the weld and the receiving of a pulse through the weld indicating a clear path free from discontinuities (Fig. 10.2).

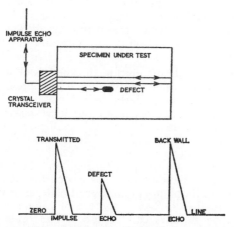

FIG. 10.1. PULSE REFLEXION METHOD SHOWING CATHODE RAY TRACE

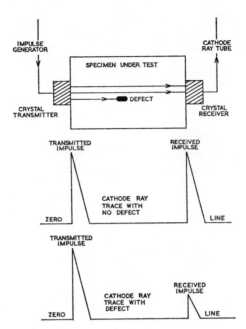

FIG. 10.2. TRANSMISSION METHOD SHOWING CATHODE RAY TRACE

TESTING WITH X-RAYS AND GAMMA RAYS (RADIOGRAPHY)

Radiographical examination is the most useful of the non-destructive tests which can be applied to butt welds for the purpose of assessing the quality of the welded joint.

When X-rays fall upon the metal, their passage is obstructed by the metal and part of the radiation is absorbed. The amount which is absorbed is dependent on the length of the metallic path traversed and hence the radiation which passes through the specimen can be employed to give an indication of any variation in effective length of the metallic path.

If, therefore, a plate of uniform thickness is exposed to X-ray radiation at right angles to the surface it will present a uniform obstacle to the radiation and a photographic film exposed under the plate would not show any preferential or local darkening after the usual processing. Where a void or non-metallic matter is present in an otherwise uniform section of metal the amount of X-ray radiation which is absorbed in this region will be less than in the case of the uniform material. More will pass through and the variation in the amount of X-ray radiation which has passed through the material can be revealed by the photographic film or plate, as seen in Fig. 10.3.

As an alternative to X-rays, the use of gamma rays produced from radioactive isotopes can be used. The equipment can be reasonably portable and radiographs of good quality can be

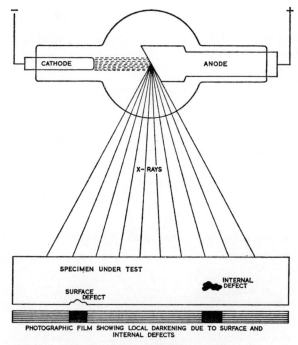

FIG. 10.3.   RADIOGRAPHICAL EXAMINATION USING X-RAYS

obtained; unfortunately the exposure times will be longer and this could be an embarrassment in populated positions.

Iridium 192, caesium 137 and cobalt 60 are some of the radio isotopes used.

QUESTIONS ON CHAPTER 10

(1) Which one of the following metals is used when producing a magnetic fluid:
- (a) Lead
- (b) Tin
- (c) Zinc
- (d) Iron?

(2) Which one of the following non-destructive tests would be used to examine a completed weld for surface defects:
- (a) Ultrasonic
- (b) Dye penetrant
- (c) Radiography
- (d) Acoustics?

(3) Which one of the following metals is unsuitable for testing with ultrasonics:
- (a) Copper
- (b) Aluminium
- (c) Cast iron
- (d) Stainless steel?

(4) If a fabricated vessel is to be pressure tested using water it will come under the heading of:
- (a) Ultrasonics
- (b) Pneumatics
- (c) Hydraulics
- (d) Radiographics.

(5) Which of the following tests is of a destructive nature:
- (a) Ultrasonic examination
- (b) Radiographic examination
- (c) Macroscopic examination
- (d) Electromagnetic examination?

(Answers on page 100)

APPENDICES

APPENDIX
1

TYPICAL COMPOSITIONS AND APPLICATIONS OF PLAIN CARBON STEELS

LOW CARBON STEELS (MILD STEELS)

Carbon	Silicon	Manganese
0·15% to 0·25%	0·10% to 0·30%	0·50% to 1·00%

Phosphorus	Sulphur
0·05% max.	0·05% max.

Hot and cold rolled strip, bar, and sheet.
Ship and boiler plate, solid-drawn tube.
Steel sections, joists, channels, angles, etc.
Stampings, pressings and drop forgings.
Tin plate, screws, and machine parts.

MEDIUM CARBON STEELS

Carbon	Silicon	Manganese
0·25% to 0·50%	0·10% to 0·30%	0·50% to 1·00%

Phosphorus	Sulphur
0·05% max	0·05% max.

Bright drawn strip and bar.
High tensile tubes and boiler drums.
Agricultural tools and die blocks.
Shafts, gears, fish plates and axles.
Connecting-rods, crankshafts, and wire rope.

HIGH CARBON STEELS. (Tool steels 0·90% to 1·40% carbon).

Carbon	Silicon	Manganese
0·50% to 1·40%	0·10% to 0·30%	0·50% max.

Phosphorus	Sulphur
0·05% max.	0·05% max.

Railway tyres and springs.
Automobile springs and bumpers.
Saws, hammers, drills, punches, riveters and chisels.
Shear blades, dies, cutters, reamers, razors and axes.
Woodwork tools, turning tools, planing tools and files.

APPENDIX
2

TEMPERING TEMPERATURES AND COLOURS FOR PLAIN CARBON STEEL TOOLS

TEMPERATURE	COLOUR	TYPE OF ARTICLE
220°C	Pale straw	Lathe tools and parting tools for light work, scrapers, and slotting tools.
230°C	Medium straw	Lathe tools, screwing dies and hammer faces.
240°C	Dark straw	Drills, reamers, shear blades, milling cutters and boring cutters.
250°C	Brown	Taps, punches, dies, rock drills, knife blades, and shear blades for metal.
260°C	Brownish-purple	Plane blades, twist drills, punches, snaps, reamers and stone-cutting tools.
270°C	Purple	Press tools, surgical tools, axes, flat drills, augers, and gimlets.
280°C	Dark purple	Cold chisels, wood chisels, setts for steel and various wood cutters.
290°C	Mauve	Cold chisels for soft iron, screwdrivers, and various small metal-work tools.
300°C	Blue	Wood-working saws, and springs for various mechanical purposes.

APPENDIX
3

ETCHING REAGENTS FOR MACROSCOPIC EXAMINATION OF FERROUS AND NON-FERROUS METALS AND ALLOYS

MATERIAL	COMPOSITION OF ETCHANT	PREPARATION DETAILS
Plain carbon steels	50cc hydrochloric acid 50cc water	Use in boiling condition. Will reveal weld structure cracks and porosity.
	10cc nitric acid 90cc water	Use in cold condition. Will reveal grain structure in weld and parent metals.
	10cc ammonium persulphate 90cc water	Use as a cold swab. Will reveal grain growth in the heat-affected zone.
Stainless steels	15cc hydrochloric acid 5cc nitric acid 100cc water	Use in cold condition. Will reveal grain structure in weld and parent metals.
Aluminium and its alloys	10cc hydrofluoric acid 1cc nitric acid 200cc water	Use in cold condition. Will reveal grain structure in weld and parent metals.
Copper and its alloys	25g ferric chloride 25cc hydrochloric acid 100cc water	Use in cold condition. Will reveal grain structure in weld and parent metals.

All etching reagents should be made up by a responsible student, laboratory steward, workshop steward, or by the teacher himself.

APPENDIX
4

COLOURS CORRESPONDING TO VARIOUS TEMPERATURES

COLOUR	TEMPERATURE °C
Red	
visible in dark	400
visible in twilight	475
visible in daylight	525
visible in sunlight	580
Dark Red	700
Dull Cherry	800
Cherry	900
Bright Cherry	1000
Orange—Red	1100
Yellow	1200
Yellow—White	1300
White	1400
Brilliant White	1500

APPENDIX
5

50 FAMILIAR ELEMENTS

ELEMENT	SYMBOL	ELEMENT	SYMBOL
Aluminium	Al	Mercury	Hg
Antimony	Sb	Molybdenum	Mo
Argon	A	Neon	Ne
Arsenic	As	Nickel	Ni
Beryllium	Be	Niobium	Nb
Bismuth	Bi	Nitrogen	N
Boron	B	Oxygen	O
Cadmium	Cd	Phosphorus	P
Calcium	Ca	Platinum	Pt
Carbon	C	Potassium	K
Chlorine	Cl	Radium	Ra
Chromium	Cr	Silicon	Si
Cobalt	Co	Silver	Ag
Copper	Cu	Sodium	Na
Gold	Au	Strontium	Sr
Helium	He	Sulphur	S
Hydrogen	H	Thorium	Th
Iodine	I	Tin	Sn
Iridium	Ir	Titanium	Ti
Iron	Fe	Tungsten	W
Krypton	Kr	Uranium	U
Lead	Pb	Vanadium	V
Lithium	Li	Xenon	Xe
Magnesium	Mg	Zinc	Zn
Manganese	Mn	Zirconium	Zr

APPENDIX
6

ARC WELDING ELECTRODES

The core wire

The type of steel generally used is that known as **rimmed steel.** This has a sulphur and phosphorus content not exceeding 0·04 per cent for each.

Ingots of rimmed steel are heterogeneous; the outer rim is of relatively pure steel and the core contains finely dispersed oxides.

These oxides act as thermionic emitters in the core of the wire produced from such ingots and help to stabilize the arc.

Attempts to weld with wire produced from **killed steel,** which is free from these oxides, results in an unstable arc which is very difficult to maintain.

CLASSIFICATION OF GAS WELDING RODS AND WIRES

A1. General purpose low carbon steel (mild steel) filler rods and wires.

Chemical composition:

CARBON:	0·10% max.	SULPHUR:	0·05% max.
MANGANESE:	0·60% max.	PHOSPHORUS:	0·05% max.
NICKEL:	0·25% max.		

A2. Low carbon steel filler rods and wires other than general use.

Chemical composition:

CARBON:	0·10% min/0·20% max.
MANGANESE:	1·00% min/1·60% max.
SILICON:	0·10% min/0·35% max.
SULPHUR:	0·04% max.
PHOSPHORUS:	0·04% max.

When the carbon content is within the range of 0·10% to 0·12% the manganese is not less than 1·20%.

A3. Medium tensile steel filler rods and wires.

Chemical composition:

CARBON:	0·25% min/0·30% max.
SILICON:	0·30% min/0·50% max.
MANGANESE:	1·30% min/1·60% max.
NICKEL, if present:	0·25% max.
CHROMIUM, if present:	0·25% max.
SULPHUR:	0·05% max.
PHOSPHORUS:	0·05% max.

APPENDIX
7

THE STRENGTH OF THE WELDED JOINT

The main criterion in evaluating the strength of a welded joint is the throat thickness of the weld deposit. In the case of a butt joint it is the length of the perpendicular from the root to a line joining the upper corners of the parent metals. In the case of a fillet joint it is the length of a straight line at 45° from the inside corner to a point where it cuts a straight line running at right angles to it, and bisecting the toes of the weld deposit. The thickness of weld metal above or below the throat is considered to be the reinforcement, and its area is ignored when calculating the strength of the welded joint.

This design strength can be ascertained by dividing the load that is to be put upon the joint by the sum of the throat thickness, multiplied by the length of the joint.

The strength thus obtained should at least be equal to the permissible safe working strength, which can be deduced from the considerations taken into account of the physical and mechanical properties of the joint material and the nature of the load (dead or live) that is to be put upon this material during service conditions.

APPENDIX
8

THE RESULT OF SEVERE WEATHER CONDITIONS ON WELDING

If welding is executed on metal surfaces at low temperatures the resultant structures of the metals could be of a very hard and brittle nature, as a direct result of the rapid cooling that would take place. These structural changes would be most severe with materials such as low alloy high tensile steels which are being welded under these cold conditions, unless adequate pre-heat and post-heat treatments are carried out.

Damp or wet conditions can be detrimental to the quality of welds as a result of oxygen and hydrogen contamination. These gases can be liberated during the dissociation of the water molecule. The influence of extreme heat sources such as the electric arc is responsible for the breakdown of such compound atoms.

The effects of high winds on the welding operation can cause a lack of stability of the welding arc as well as a disruption of the gaseous shield surrounding the arc which could lead to severe atmosphere contamination of the molten weld metal.

APPENDIX
9

CARBON EQUIVALENTS

The carbon equivalent formula which indicates equivalent hardenability in alloy steels can be of prime importance as a weldability classification particularly in connection with cold cracking tendencies.

As the carbon equivalent value increases, the susceptibility to cracking also increases and so the weldability of a particular alloy steel decreases.

The carbon equivalent formula in general use is:

$$CE = C\% + \frac{Mn\%}{6} + \frac{(Cr + Mo + V)\%}{5} + \frac{(Ni + Cu)\%}{15}$$

To determine the carbon equivalent of a particular alloy steel, the chemical symbols in the formula are substituted by the percentages of the respective elements in the steel. An example of the application of the formula is given below.

Alloy steel analysis:

CARBON	$C = 0.2\%$
MANGANESE	$Mn = 1.5\%$
CHROMIUM	$Cr = 0.025\%$
MOLYBDENUM	$Mo = 0.015\%$
NICKEL	$Ni = 0.04\%$
COPPER	$Cu = 0.04\%$

$$CE = 0.2 + \frac{1.5}{6} + \frac{0.025 + 0.015}{5} + \frac{0.04 + 0.04}{15}$$

$$CE = (0.2 + 0.25 + 0.008 + 0.005) = 0.463$$

Therefore the carbon equivalent $CE = 0.463\%$

Note that silicon and the impurities phosphorous and sulphur are not considered when using this carbon equivalent formula.

APPENDIX
10

Thermo-Electric Pyrometers

These instruments work on the theory that an electric current can be produced by thermal means alone.

If two wires, each of a different metal, are joined together at both pairs of free ends, and heat is applied to one junction, whilst the other junction is kept cold, an electromotive force will be set up, provided the wires are insulated from each other throughout their length.

If a millivoltmeter is now connected across the cold junction, the resultant electromotive force flowing in the circuit due to the hot junction can be measured (Fig. A.1), and it is found that a rise in temperature at the hot junction will cause an increase in the flow of electric current, the ratio always being constant.

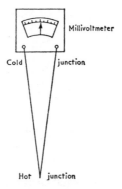

FIG. A.1.   THERMO-ELECTRIC COUPLE

The two dissimilar metallic wires are termed the **thermocouple.** They can consist of iridium, rhodium, nickel and nickel alloys, etc., and they are contained in a refractory tube to prevent contamination from gases and slags in the furnace.

The millivoltmeter is generally a considerable distance from the furnace, so compensating leads are used which have the same thermo-electric constants as the "couple" but are of less expensive metals (Fig. A.2).

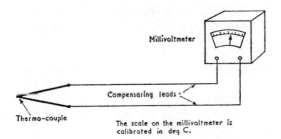

FIG. A.2. THE THERMO-ELECTRIC PYROMETER

ANSWERS TO QUESTIONS
SET AT END OF CHAPTERS

Chapter 1	Chapter 2
No. 1 (c)	No. 1 (c)
2 (b)	2 (c)
3 (a)	3 (a)
4 (b)	4 (b)
5 (b)	5 (c)

Chapter 3	Chapter 4
No. 1 (b)	No. 1 (a)
2 (d)	2 (d)
3 (b)	3 (c)
4 (a)	4 (a)
5 (a)	5 (b)

Chapter 5	Chapter 6
No. 1 (b)	No. 1 (a)
2 (b)	2 (b)
3 (a)	3 (b)
4 (c)	4 (b)
5 (c)	5 (b)

Chapter 7	Chapter 8
No. 1 (c)	No. 1 (c)
2 (b)	2 (c)
3 (c)	3 (d)
4 (a)	4 (a)
5 (c)	5 (d)

Chapter 9	Chapter 10
No. 1 (b)	No. 1 (d)
2 (b)	2 (b)
3 (a)	3 (c)
4 (b)	4 (c)
5 (a)	5 (c)

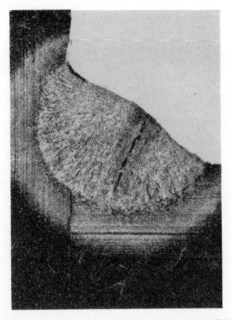

FIG. A × 2.   PHOTOMACROGRAPH OF A FILLET WELD JOINING TWO HIGH-ALLOY
STEELS SHOWING HOT CRACKING WITHIN THE WELD DEPOSIT

FIG. B × 2.   PHOTOMACROGRAPH OF A FILLET WELD JOINING TWO LOW-ALLOY
STEELS SHOWING HARD-ZONE OR UNDER-BEAD CRACKING IN
THE HEAT-AFFECTED ZONE

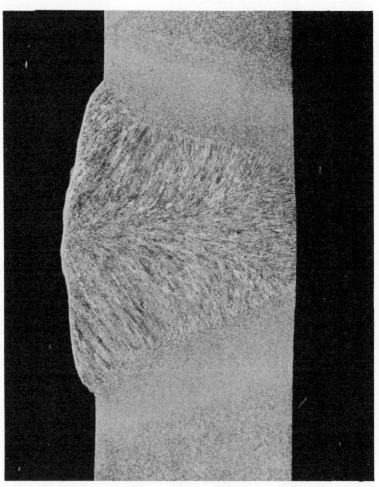

FIG. C × 2.   PHOTOMACROGRAPH OF A SINGLE VEE BUTT WELD JOINING TWO LOW CARBON STEEL PLATES
BY THE SUBMERGED ARC PROCESS

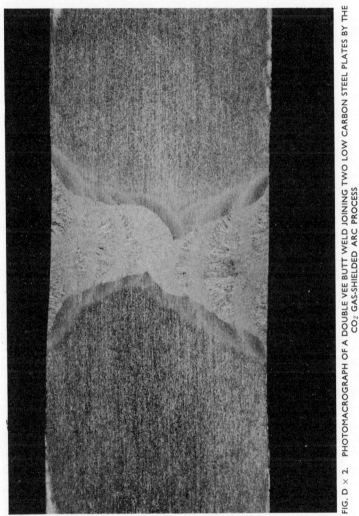

FIG. D × 2.   PHOTOMACROGRAPH OF A DOUBLE VEE BUTT WELD JOINING TWO LOW CARBON STEEL PLATES BY THE CO_2 GAS-SHIELDED ARC PROCESS

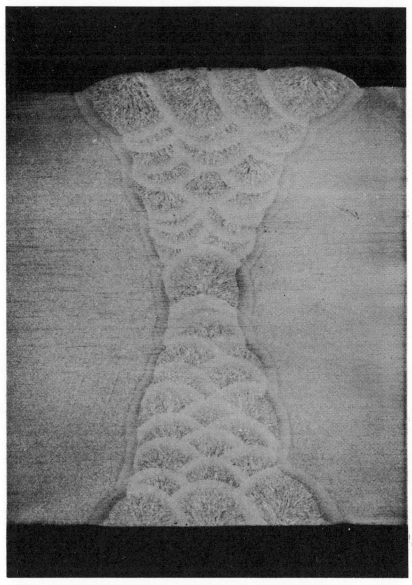

FIG. E × 1½. PHOTOMACROGRAPH OF A DOUBLE VEE BUTT WELD JOINING TWO LOW CARBON
STEEL PLATES BY THE SUBMERGED ARC PROCESS

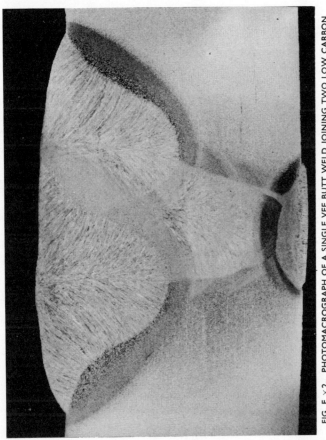

FIG. F ×2. PHOTOMACROGRAPH OF A SINGLE VEE BUTT WELD JOINING TWO LOW CARBON STEEL PLATES BY THE SUBMERGED ARC PROCESS

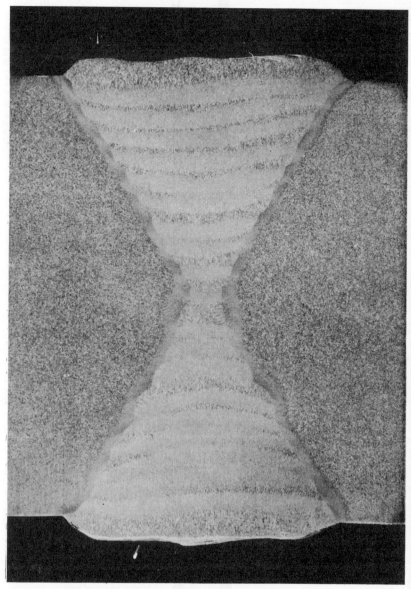

FIG. G × 1½.   PHOTOMACROGRAPH OF A VERTICAL DOUBLE VEE BUTT WELD JOINING TWO
LOW CARBON STEEL PLATES BY THE MANUAL METAL ARC PROCESS

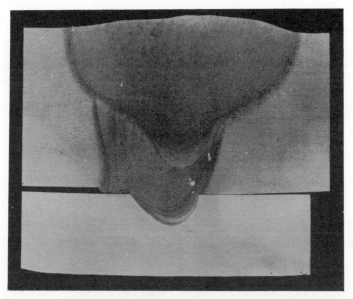

FIG. H × 2. PHOTOMACROGRAPH OF A SINGLE VEE BUTT WELD WITH BACKING
STRIP JOINING TWO ALUMINIUM ALLOYS BY THE TUNGSTEN
INERT GAS PROCESS

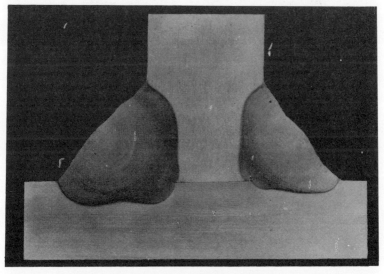

FIG. J × 2. PHOTOMACROGRAPH OF A HORIZONTAL-VERTICAL FILLET JOINING
TWO ALUMINIUM ALLOYS BY THE AUTOMATIC SIGMA PROCESS

FIG. K × 15.   PHOTOMACROGRAPH OF A BUTT WELD JOINING TWO MILD STEEL SHEETS BY THE OXY-ACETYLENE GAS WELDING PROCESS

INDEX